by Dav Pilkey

SCHOLASTIC

FOR JAMES MARSHALL

First published in the USA in 1995 by Scholastic Inc
This edition first published in the UK in 2009 by Scholastic Children's Books
Euston House, 24 Eversholt Street
London NW1 1DB
a division of Scholastic Ltd
www.scholastic.co.uk
London ~ New York ~ Toronto ~ Sydney ~ Auckland
Mexico City ~ New Delhi ~ Hong Kong

Text and illustrations copyright © 1995 Dav Pilkey

ISBN 978 1407 11202 2

10 9 8 7 6 5 4 3 2 1

It was December 24th, and the Dumb Bunnies were getting ready for Easter.

Momma Bunny was stuffing the turkey,

Poppa Bunny was nailing up valentines...

...and Baby Bunny was giving eggnog
to a merry group of carollers.
"That's my boy," said Poppa Bunny.

Soon it was time for Poppa Bunny to go and pick out an Easter tree. So he put on his winter clothes and got ready to leave.

"Can I help you pick the Easter tree?" asked
Baby Bunny. "I'm very good at picking things!"
"I can see that," said Poppa Bunny.

So Poppa and Baby Bunny went out and found
a wonderful tree. It was right in their neighbour's
front yard.

Poppa Bunny took out his saw and chopped
the tree down. Chop! Chop! Chop!

Then Poppa Bunny carried the Easter tree home.
(Baby Bunny helped a little bit.)

Later, Poppa and Baby Bunny put up the tree, while Momma Bunny brought three big boxes down from the basement.

"Now comes the fun part," said Momma Bunny.

"I get to put on the lights," said Poppa Bunny.
"I get to put on the ornaments," said Momma Bunny.
"And I get to put on the tinsel," said Baby Bunny.

So they did.

Then it was time for Thanksgiving
dinner, and everyone pitched in to help.
Poppa Bunny carved the turkey,
Momma Bunny tossed the salad...

...and Baby Bunny cut the cheese.
"That's my boy," said Poppa Bunny.

After supper, it was time for the Bunnies
to celebrate their dumb holiday traditions.

First, they painted Easter eggs.

Then they watched a little football
on the TV.

And finally, they ran to the fireplace
to hang up their stockings.

"Maybe we should have taken our stockings *off,* first," said Momma Bunny.

All night long, the Dumb Bunnies hung around
and talked about the true meaning of Easter.
"I hope the Easter Bunny brings me a million
dollars," said Momma Bunny.

"Oh, yeah?" said Poppa Bunny. "Well, *I* hope the Easter Bunny brings me a *THOUSAND* dollars!"

"I hope the Easter Bunny brings me a balloon," said Baby Bunny.

"Now don't be greedy," said Momma and Poppa Bunny.

"Sorry," said Baby Bunny.

That night while they slept, the Easter
Bunny came in a shiny red minivan...

...pulled by eight flying pilgrims.

The Easter Bunny gathered up dozens
of the most beautiful eggs he had...

...and dropped them down the chimney.
"Ho, ho, ho — look out below!" he yelled.

The next morning, the Dumb Bunnies were thrilled to see what the Easter Bunny had brought them.

They had to admit that this was the most terrible
Easter they had ever had...

...and they hoped their next Easter would be even *worse!*

INTRODUCTION ...

A few points about this revision guide ...

- It is matched perfectly to the new specification from AQA:

<u>SCIENCE: DOUBLE AWARD COORDINATED - Specification B</u>

So it contains everything the pupil needs to know, ...

... and nothing more.

- The 'Contents' pages are cross-referenced to the specification reference.

- Each section is condensed into a single 'Key Points' page. This enables a quick final recap prior to examination and also builds pupils' confidence in that they can see their task before them on a single page.

- Each section concludes with a set of summary questions. These are, of necessity, brief but can be supplemented by our brilliant volume of 'pupil worksheets' which are written page for page to this guide (see inside back cover).

- Slang words and colloquialisms are avoided in favour of plain, good old-fashioned English.

- The new layout, with improved diagrams, provides a more spacious, user-friendly feel.

- 'Cell Activity' and 'Green Plants As Organisms' are combined to form one 'Key Points' page and 'Summary Questions' section.

- The reduction in the amount of 'Higher' material in the new specification means that it makes more sense than ever before to combine both 'Higher' and 'Foundation' material in the one guide. This, of course, allows much greater flexibility in switching between tiers.

> **HIGHER TIER**
> All the 'Higher' material is clearly indicated by RED boxes.

Mary James

Mary James – **Editor**

• CONTENTS

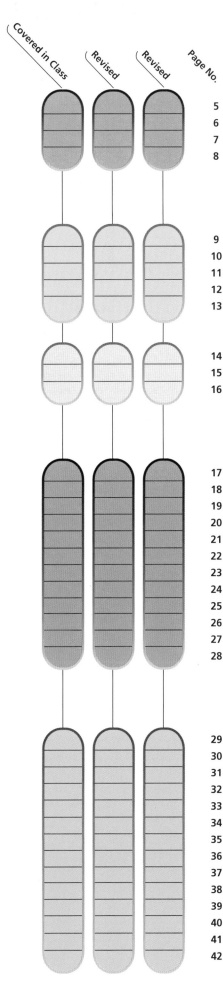

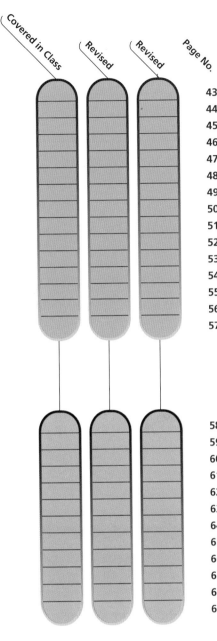

Covered in Class Revised Revised Page No.

*Numbers in brackets refer to Specification reference numbers

HOW TO USE THIS REVISION GUIDE

- Don't just sit back and read this guide. Learn actively by constantly testing yourself without looking at the text.

- When you have revised a small sub-section or a diagram, PLACE A BOLD TICK AGAINST IT, and also tick the 'Covered In Class' and 'Revised' sections of the contents pages as you progress.
  This is great for your self-confidence.

- Jot down anything which will help you to remember – no matter how trivial it may seem.

- Use the actual pages within a section for your revision and link them to the information in the 'Key Points' pages. Only use the 'Key Points' pages on their own for a last minute recap before your examination.

HIGHER TIER
ONLY PUPILS DOING HIGHER TIER SHOULD REVISE THE MATERIAL IN THE RED BOXES.

SOME IMPORTANT FACTS ABOUT YOUR EXAMINATION

- You will have THREE PAPERS lasting 1 HOUR 30 MINUTES EACH.

- Each paper will consist of 90 marks and represent $26^2/_3$ % of the total marks available.

- All papers will consist of compulsory structured questions of different lengths, incorporating calculations and data-response, and will provide opportunities for answers written in continuous prose.
  The marking of these will take into account the quality of written communication.

- Candidates may use a calculator for all three papers.

  PAPER 1: LIFE PROCESSES AND LIVING THINGS
  PAPER 2: MATERIALS AND THEIR PROPERTIES
  PAPER 3: PHYSICAL PROCESSES

Typical Plant And Animal Cells

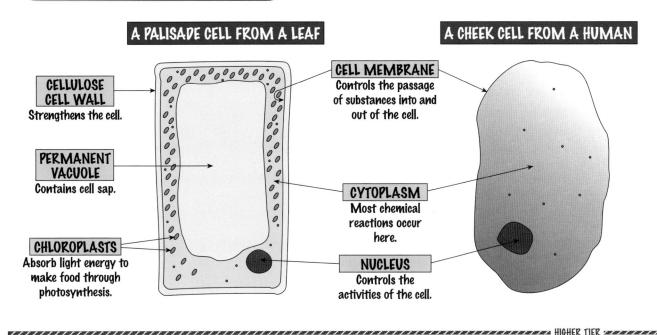

A PALISADE CELL FROM A LEAF

A CHEEK CELL FROM A HUMAN

CELLULOSE CELL WALL
Strengthens the cell.

PERMANENT VACUOLE
Contains cell sap.

CHLOROPLASTS
Absorb light energy to make food through photosynthesis.

CELL MEMBRANE
Controls the passage of substances into and out of the cell.

CYTOPLASM
Most chemical reactions occur here.

NUCLEUS
Controls the activities of the cell.

HIGHER TIER

Most cells are made up of water containing dissolved substances. These substances are usually in the process of being made into something which the cell needs. This involves chemical reactions controlled by ENZYMES. These often occur in structures called MITOCHONDRIA in the cytoplasm where most of the energy is released via RESPIRATION. (see P.24)

Types Of Animal Cell

Some cells are highly SPECIALISED to do a particular job ...

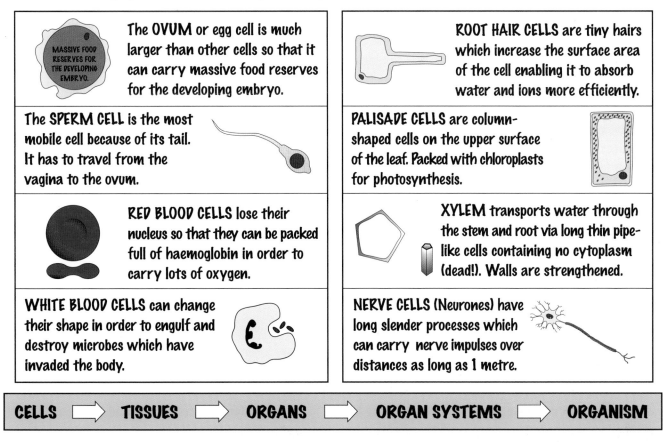

MASSIVE FOOD RESERVES FOR THE DEVELOPING EMBRYO.

The OVUM or egg cell is much larger than other cells so that it can carry massive food reserves for the developing embryo.

ROOT HAIR CELLS are tiny hairs which increase the surface area of the cell enabling it to absorb water and ions more efficiently.

The SPERM CELL is the most mobile cell because of its tail. It has to travel from the vagina to the ovum.

PALISADE CELLS are column-shaped cells on the upper surface of the leaf. Packed with chloroplasts for photosynthesis.

RED BLOOD CELLS lose their nucleus so that they can be packed full of haemoglobin in order to carry lots of oxygen.

XYLEM transports water through the stem and root via long thin pipe-like cells containing no cytoplasm (dead!). Walls are strengthened.

WHITE BLOOD CELLS can change their shape in order to engulf and destroy microbes which have invaded the body.

NERVE CELLS (Neurones) have long slender processes which can carry nerve impulses over distances as long as 1 metre.

CELLS ⟹ TISSUES ⟹ ORGANS ⟹ ORGAN SYSTEMS ⟹ ORGANISM

Diffusion

Because cells are living things, they have to constantly replace substances which are used up (food, oxygen) and remove other substances which would otherwise accumulate (carbon dioxide, waste products).

These substances, plus simple sugars and ions, pass easily through cell membranes.

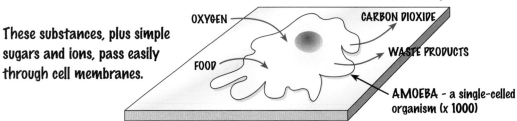

OXYGEN — CARBON DIOXIDE — WASTE PRODUCTS — FOOD — AMOEBA - a single-celled organism (x 1000)

Even simple, single-celled animals, like the amoeba above, need to do this. Happily, this can take place automatically, without the need for energy, in a process called DIFFUSION.

> DIFFUSION is ...
> ... the spreading of the particles of a gas, or of any substance in solution, ...
> ... resulting in a net movement from a region where they are at a higher concentration ...
> ... to a region where they are at a lower concentration.

Diffusion can be demonstrated in the following ways ...

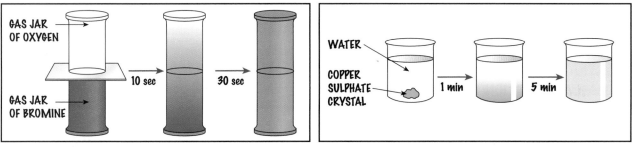

GAS JAR OF OXYGEN — 10 sec — 30 sec — GAS JAR OF BROMINE

WATER — COPPER SULPHATE CRYSTAL — 1 min — 5 min

> The greater the difference in concentration, the faster the rate of diffusion.

So in the example of oxygen and the amoeba, there's lots of oxygen outside the amoeba but much less inside, because it's being used up in respiration. So the higher concentration outside results in oxygen 'spreading' (DIFFUSING) into the amoeba across the cell membrane.

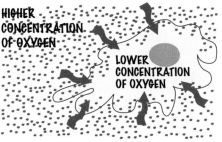

HIGHER CONCENTRATION OF OXYGEN — LOWER CONCENTRATION OF OXYGEN

Examples In Living Organisms

Surfaces across which gases are exchanged are often specialised in organisms by having LARGE SURFACE AREAS to increase the rate at which diffusion can occur.
These are examples of ADAPTATION.

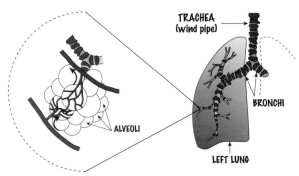

TRACHEA (wind pipe) — BRONCHI — ALVEOLI — LEFT LUNG

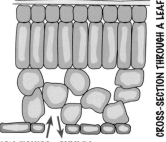

CROSS-SECTION THROUGH A LEAF

CARBON DIOXIDE OXYGEN

The ALVEOLI in the lungs provide a massive surface area for exchange of oxygen and carbon dioxide. These both diffuse across the cell membranes of the alveoli.

The spaces inside leaves provide a big surface area for exchange of carbon dioxide and oxygen. Carbon dioxide diffuses into the leaf and then across the cell membranes and vice versa for oxygen.

Osmosis

OSMOSIS is ... the **DIFFUSION OF WATER** ...

... from a **DILUTE SOLUTION** ...

... to a **MORE CONCENTRATED SOLUTION** ...

... through a **PARTIALLY PERMEABLE MEMBRANE** that ...

... **ALLOWS THE PASSAGE OF WATER MOLECULES BUT NOT SOLUTE MOLECULES.**

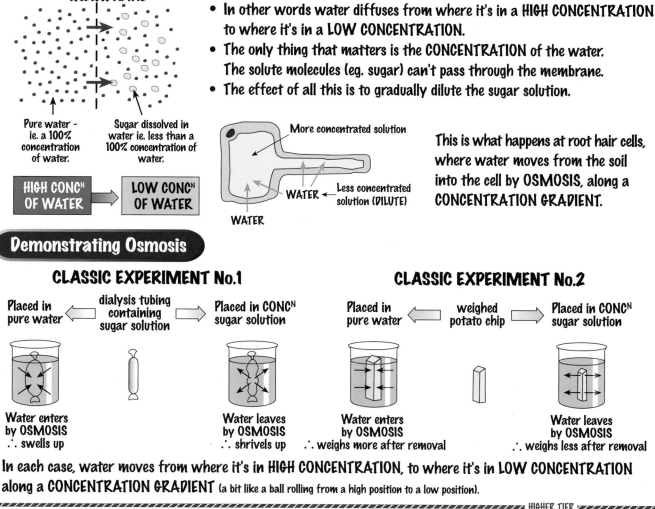

MEMBRANE

Pure water - ie. a 100% concentration of water.

Sugar dissolved in water ie. less than a 100% concentration of water.

HIGH CONCⁿ OF WATER → **LOW CONCⁿ OF WATER**

- In other words water diffuses from where it's in a **HIGH CONCENTRATION** to where it's in a **LOW CONCENTRATION**.
- The only thing that matters is the **CONCENTRATION** of the water. The solute molecules (eg. sugar) can't pass through the membrane.
- The effect of all this is to gradually dilute the sugar solution.

More concentrated solution

WATER ← Less concentrated solution (DILUTE)

WATER

This is what happens at root hair cells, where water moves from the soil into the cell by OSMOSIS, along a CONCENTRATION GRADIENT.

Demonstrating Osmosis

CLASSIC EXPERIMENT No.1

Placed in pure water ← dialysis tubing containing sugar solution → Placed in CONCⁿ sugar solution

Water enters by OSMOSIS ∴ swells up

Water leaves by OSMOSIS ∴ shrivels up

CLASSIC EXPERIMENT No.2

Placed in pure water ← weighed potato chip → Placed in CONCⁿ sugar solution

Water enters by OSMOSIS ∴ weighs more after removal

Water leaves by OSMOSIS ∴ weighs less after removal

In each case, water moves from where it's in **HIGH CONCENTRATION**, to where it's in **LOW CONCENTRATION** along a **CONCENTRATION GRADIENT** (a bit like a ball rolling from a high position to a low position).

— HIGHER TIER —

Active Transport

- Substances are sometimes absorbed **AGAINST A CONCENTRATION GRADIENT**.
- Plants absorb ions from very dilute solutions in this way ie. **ACTIVELY** (see diagram below).
- This takes place in the opposite direction to which normal diffusion would occur.
- This process of **ACTIVE TRANSPORT** requires the use of **ENERGY FROM RESPIRATION** ...
  ... just in the same way that pushing a ball up a hill would take energy.

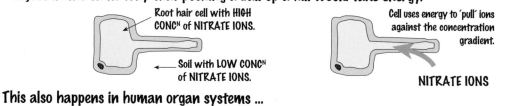

Root hair cell with HIGH CONCⁿ of NITRATE IONS.

Soil with LOW CONCⁿ of NITRATE IONS.

Cell uses energy to 'pull' ions against the concentration gradient.

NITRATE IONS

This also happens in human organ systems ...

- ... sugar may be absorbed from low concentration in the intestines, and ...
- ... also from low concentration in the kidney tubules. Here, the body recovers all the sugar back into the blood so that none of it is excreted in the urine.

HIGHER TIER

Many organ systems are **SPECIALISED FOR EXCHANGING MATERIALS.**

Examples In Humans

1. The <u>alveoli</u> in the lungs ...

... provide a **MASSIVE SURFACE AREA** for **EXCHANGE OF OXYGEN AND CARBON DIOXIDE.**

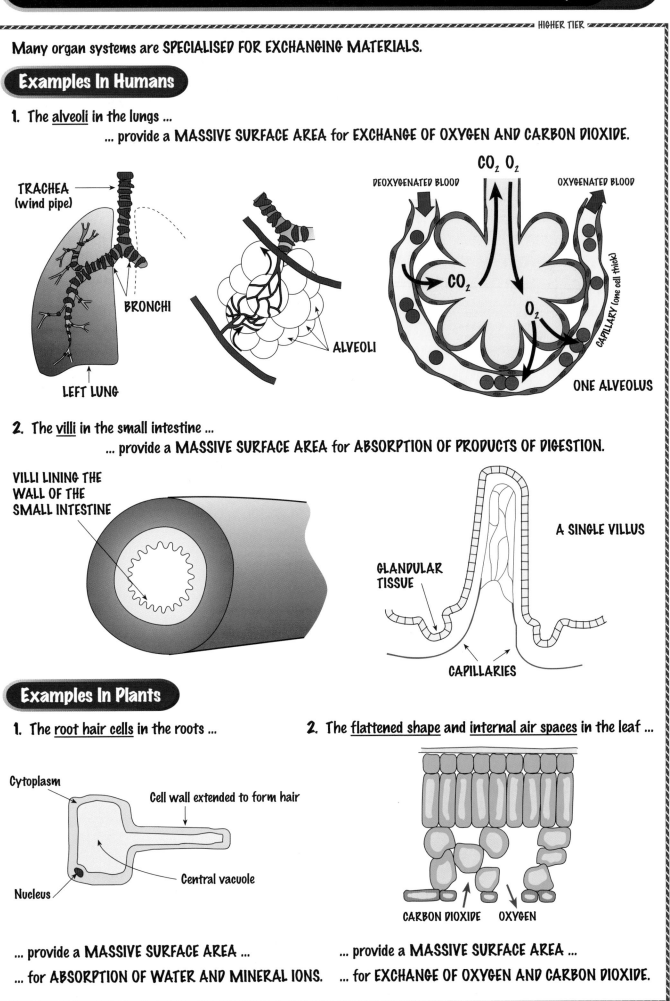

TRACHEA (wind pipe)

BRONCHI

LEFT LUNG

ALVEOLI

CO_2 O_2

DEOXYGENATED BLOOD

OXYGENATED BLOOD

CO_2

O_2

CAPILLARY (one cell thick)

ONE ALVEOLUS

2. The <u>villi</u> in the small intestine ...

... provide a **MASSIVE SURFACE AREA** for **ABSORPTION OF PRODUCTS OF DIGESTION.**

VILLI LINING THE WALL OF THE SMALL INTESTINE

A SINGLE VILLUS

GLANDULAR TISSUE

CAPILLARIES

Examples In Plants

1. The <u>root hair cells</u> in the roots ...

Cytoplasm

Cell wall extended to form hair

Central vacuole

Nucleus

... provide a **MASSIVE SURFACE AREA** ...

... for **ABSORPTION OF WATER AND MINERAL IONS.**

2. The <u>flattened shape</u> and <u>internal air spaces</u> in the leaf ...

CARBON DIOXIDE   OXYGEN

... provide a **MASSIVE SURFACE AREA** ...

... for **EXCHANGE OF OXYGEN AND CARBON DIOXIDE.**

Making Food Using Energy From The Sun

Green plants don't absorb food from the soil. They make their own, using sunlight. This is called PHOTOSYNTHESIS, which actually means 'making through light'. It occurs in the cells of green plants, which are exposed to light.

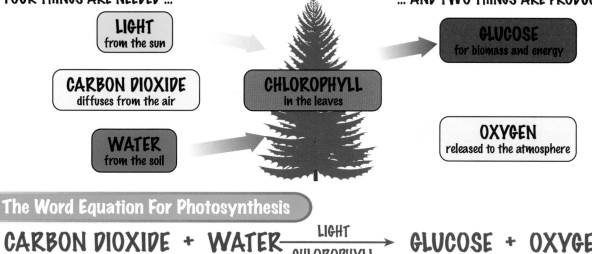

FOUR THINGS ARE NEEDED ...

LIGHT from the sun

CARBON DIOXIDE diffuses from the air

WATER from the soil

CHLOROPHYLL in the leaves

... AND TWO THINGS ARE PRODUCED ...

GLUCOSE for biomass and energy

OXYGEN released to the atmosphere

The Word Equation For Photosynthesis

$$\text{CARBON DIOXIDE} + \text{WATER} \xrightarrow[\text{CHLOROPHYLL}]{\text{LIGHT}} \text{GLUCOSE} + \text{OXYGEN}$$

Some of the glucose produced in photosynthesis is used immediately by the plant to provide energy via RESPIRATION. However, much of the glucose is converted into INSOLUBLE STARCH for storage in the stem, leaves or roots.

Factors Affecting Photosynthesis

In practice, TEMPERATURE, CARBON DIOXIDE CONCENTRATION and LIGHT INTENSITY can interact to limit the rate of photosynthesis. Any one of them, at a particular time, may be the limiting factor.

EFFECT OF TEMPERATURE

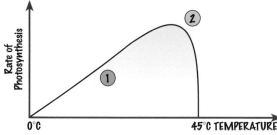

Rate of Photosynthesis

0°C   45°C TEMPERATURE

① As the temperature rises so does the rate of photosynthesis. This means temperature is limiting the rate of photosynthesis.

② As the temperature approaches **45°C** the enzymes controlling photosynthesis start to be destroyed and the rate of photosynthesis eventually declines to zero.

EFFECT OF CARBON DIOXIDE CONCENTRATION

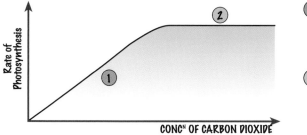

Rate of Photosynthesis

CONCⁿ OF CARBON DIOXIDE

① As the carbon dioxide concentration rises so does the rate of photosynthesis. This means carbon dioxide is limiting the rate of photosynthesis.

② Rise in carbon dioxide now has no effect. Carbon dioxide is no longer the limiting factor. This means SUNLIGHT or TEMPERATURE must be the limiting factor.

EFFECT OF LIGHT INTENSITY

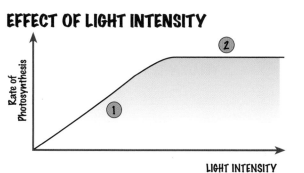

Rate of Photosynthesis

LIGHT INTENSITY

① As the light intensity increases so does the rate of photosynthesis. This means light intensity is limiting the rate of photosynthesis.

② Rise in light intensity now has no effect. Light intensity is no longer the limiting factor.
This means CARBON DIOXIDE or TEMPERATURE must be the limiting factor.

Energy Use In Plants

The glucose produced in photosynthesis can be immediately respired to produce energy.
Some of this energy is used to build up SMALLER MOLECULES INTO LARGER MOLECULES ...

1 CONVERSION OF SUGARS INTO STARCH. The plant does this because starch is an insoluble carbohydrate and therefore can be stored in cells without causing large amounts of water to accumulate as a result of OSMOSIS.

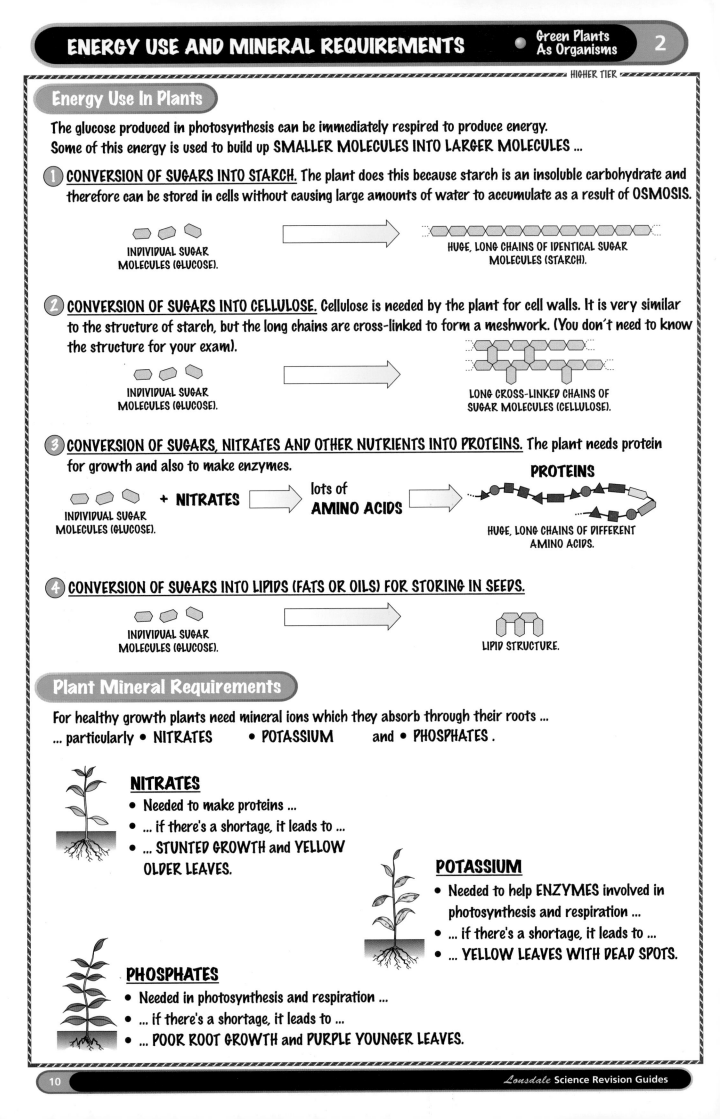

INDIVIDUAL SUGAR
MOLECULES (GLUCOSE).

HUGE, LONG CHAINS OF IDENTICAL SUGAR
MOLECULES (STARCH).

2 CONVERSION OF SUGARS INTO CELLULOSE. Cellulose is needed by the plant for cell walls. It is very similar to the structure of starch, but the long chains are cross-linked to form a meshwork. (You don't need to know the structure for your exam).

INDIVIDUAL SUGAR
MOLECULES (GLUCOSE).

LONG CROSS-LINKED CHAINS OF
SUGAR MOLECULES (CELLULOSE).

3 CONVERSION OF SUGARS, NITRATES AND OTHER NUTRIENTS INTO PROTEINS. The plant needs protein for growth and also to make enzymes.

INDIVIDUAL SUGAR
MOLECULES (GLUCOSE).

+ NITRATES

lots of
AMINO ACIDS

PROTEINS

HUGE, LONG CHAINS OF DIFFERENT
AMINO ACIDS.

4 CONVERSION OF SUGARS INTO LIPIDS (FATS OR OILS) FOR STORING IN SEEDS.

INDIVIDUAL SUGAR
MOLECULES (GLUCOSE).

LIPID STRUCTURE.

Plant Mineral Requirements

For healthy growth plants need mineral ions which they absorb through their roots ...
... particularly • NITRATES   • POTASSIUM   and • PHOSPHATES .

NITRATES
• Needed to make proteins ...
• ... if there's a shortage, it leads to ...
• ... STUNTED GROWTH and YELLOW OLDER LEAVES.

POTASSIUM
• Needed to help ENZYMES involved in photosynthesis and respiration ...
• ... if there's a shortage, it leads to ...
• ... YELLOW LEAVES WITH DEAD SPOTS.

PHOSPHATES
• Needed in photosynthesis and respiration ...
• ... if there's a shortage, it leads to ...
• ... POOR ROOT GROWTH and PURPLE YOUNGER LEAVES.

The Leaf

Leaves are BROAD, THIN and FLAT with lots of INTERNAL AIR SPACES in order to make them efficient at photosynthesis by providing a large surface area for gas exchange (oxygen and carbon dioxide). This is a typical example of how exchange surfaces are adapted to their function. They also have STOMATA on their undersurface to allow CARBON DIOXIDE to diffuse in and OXYGEN to diffuse out. This however leads to loss of water vapour in a process called TRANSPIRATION.

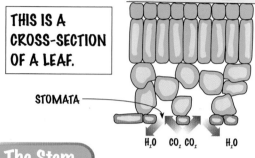

THIS IS A CROSS-SECTION OF A LEAF.

STOMATA

H_2O CO_2 CO_2 H_2O

- This WAXY LAYER (cuticle) stops too much water from just evaporating away from the leaf.
- Transpiration is more rapid in HOT, DRY or WINDY conditions, ...
  ... so plants which live in these conditions have a THICKER LAYER OF WAX.
- Water lost by transpiration must be replaced by water from the soil.

The Stem

Flowering plants have separate transport systems for water and nutrients...
- **PHLOEM TISSUE** ... transports nutrients, such as sugars, from the leaves to the rest of the plant, including the storage organs and growing regions.
- **XYLEM TISSUE** ... transports water and soluble mineral salts from the roots to the stem and leaves, to replace the water lost in transpiration and photosynthesis.

(1) Water EVAPORATES from the internal leaf cells through the STOMATA.

(2) Water passes from the XYLEM vessels to leaf cells due to OSMOSIS ...

(3) ... which 'pulls' the entire 'thread' of water in that vessel upwards by a very small amount.

(4) Water enters XYLEM from root tissue to replace water which has moved upwards.

(5) Water enters ROOT HAIR CELLS by OSMOSIS to replace water which has entered the XYLEM.

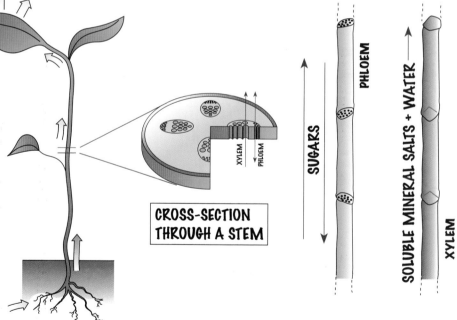

CROSS-SECTION THROUGH A STEM

PHLOEM

XYLEM

SUGARS

SOLUBLE MINERAL SALTS + WATER →

XYLEM

PHLOEM

The transpiration stream is 'powered' by evaporation of water from the leaf.

The Root

WATER enters the plant via the roots. Most of it is absorbed by the ROOT HAIR CELLS by osmosis. This water passes into the xylem vessels to replace water which is continually moving up the stem.
The surface area of the roots is increased by the presence of root hairs. This increases the rate at which they can absorb water and minerals (particularly nitrates which are needed for healthy growth) and is another typical example of how exchange surfaces are adapted to their function.

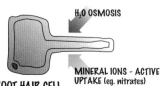

H_2O OSMOSIS

ROOT HAIR CELL

MINERAL IONS - ACTIVE UPTAKE (eg. nitrates)

Controlling Water Loss

• A leaf has holes or PORES called STOMATA, mainly on the underside of the leaf.
• Carbon dioxide and oxygen can diffuse into and out of the leaf, via these stomata, ...
  ... in order for the plant to photosynthesise.

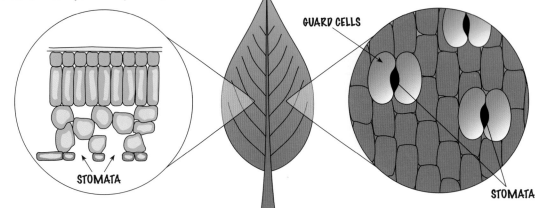

GUARD CELLS

STOMATA

STOMATA

• Unfortunately, WATER VAPOUR, from the moist surfaces of the leaf cells, also diffuses out of the stomata.
• WATER LOSS THROUGH TRANSPIRATION IS THE 'PRICE THE PLANT MUST PAY' IN ORDER TO PHOTOSYNTHESISE. However ...
• The size of the stomata is controlled by a pair of GUARD CELLS.
• If plants lose water faster than it is taken up by the roots ...
  ... the stomata can close to prevent wilting and eventual dehydration.
• In periods of intense drought, photosynthesis may be impossible, even in sunny weather, since the stomata will be closed to prevent water loss.

Maintaining Support

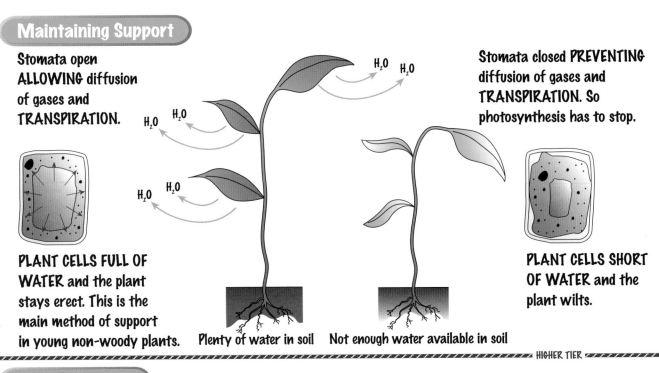

Stomata open ALLOWING diffusion of gases and TRANSPIRATION.

H_2O H_2O

H_2O H_2O

H_2O H_2O

PLANT CELLS FULL OF WATER and the plant stays erect. This is the main method of support in young non-woody plants.

Plenty of water in soil   Not enough water available in soil

Stomata closed PREVENTING diffusion of gases and TRANSPIRATION. So photosynthesis has to stop.

PLANT CELLS SHORT OF WATER and the plant wilts.

HIGHER TIER

Turgor Pressure

When water moves into plant cells by osmosis (see P.7) it increases the pressure inside the cell. This is rather like blowing up a balloon inside a cereal carton. However the cell walls are sufficiently strong to withstand the pressure and as a result the cell becomes very rigid. This is called TURGOR PRESSURE and we refer to cells with adequate supplies of water as 'maintaining their turgor' ie. staying rigid!

Plant Responses

Plants are sensitive to: • **LIGHT**   • **MOISTURE**   • **GRAVITY**
- SHOOTS grow TOWARDS LIGHT and AGAINST THE FORCE OF GRAVITY.
- ROOTS grow TOWARDS MOISTURE and in the DIRECTION OF GRAVITY.

These responses are controlled by HORMONES which coordinate and control growth.

Hormones are produced in the growing tips of shoots and roots but can then collect unevenly ...
... causing unequal growth rates in different parts of the plant.

Gravity

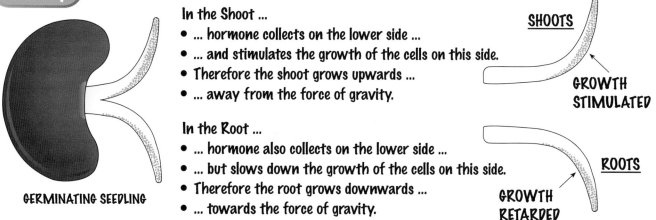

In the Shoot ...
- ... hormone collects on the lower side ...
- ... and stimulates the growth of the cells on this side.
- Therefore the shoot grows upwards ...
- ... away from the force of gravity.

In the Root ...
- ... hormone also collects on the lower side ...
- ... but slows down the growth of the cells on this side.
- Therefore the root grows downwards ...
- ... towards the force of gravity.

GERMINATING SEEDLING

SHOOTS

GROWTH STIMULATED

ROOTS

GROWTH RETARDED

The key thing to remember here is that the hormone produced in the growing tips has the OPPOSITE EFFECT in roots and shoots.
- The hormone (S)TIMULATES cell growth in (S)HOOTS, and ...
- ...(R)ETARDS cell growth in (R)OOTS.

Light

- In shoots, LIGHT causes HORMONES ...
  - ... to accumulate on the shaded part of the stem ...
    - ... which causes growth on that side ...
      - ... and the plant grows towards the sun.

LIGHT

Artificial Use Of Hormones

Farmers do this to increase their yield and to organise ripening times to suit their own convenience.
It's quite unnatural really isn't it?

- ROOTING COMPOUND - Consists of a hormone which encourages ...
                    ... the GROWTH OF ROOTS ...
                        ... in STEM CUTTINGS ...
                            ... so lots of plants can be obtained from only one.

- RIPENING HORMONE - Causes plants to ripen at set time ...
                    ... sometimes during transport.
                        Achieved by spraying.

- SELECTIVE WEEDKILLERS - Disrupt the normal growth patterns ...
                        ... of their target plants ...
                            ... leaving other plants untouched.

KEY POINTS FOR CELL ACTIVITY AND GREEN PLANTS AS ORGANISMS

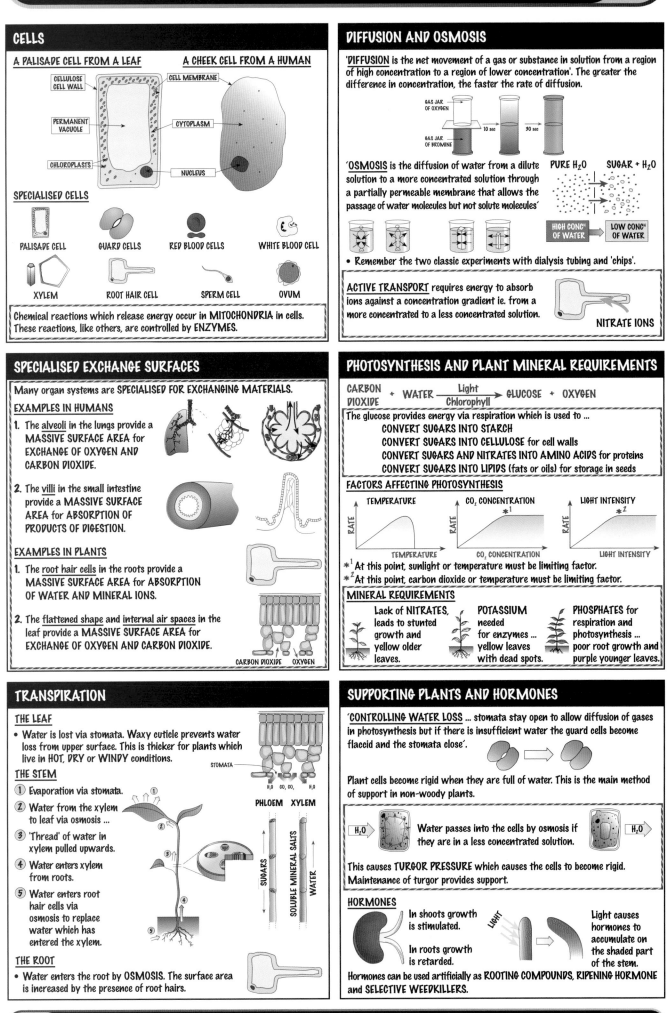

CELLS

A PALISADE CELL FROM A LEAF   A CHEEK CELL FROM A HUMAN

- CELLULOSE CELL WALL
- CELL MEMBRANE
- PERMANENT VACUOLE
- CYTOPLASM
- CHLOROPLASTS
- NUCLEUS

SPECIALISED CELLS

PALISADE CELL   GUARD CELLS   RED BLOOD CELLS   WHITE BLOOD CELL

XYLEM   ROOT HAIR CELL   SPERM CELL   OVUM

Chemical reactions which release energy occur in MITOCHONDRIA in cells. These reactions, like others, are controlled by ENZYMES.

DIFFUSION AND OSMOSIS

'DIFFUSION is the net movement of a gas or substance in solution from a region of high concentration to a region of lower concentration'. The greater the difference in concentration, the faster the rate of diffusion.

GAS JAR OF OXYGEN
GAS JAR OF BROMINE
10 sec   90 sec

'OSMOSIS is the diffusion of water from a dilute solution to a more concentrated solution through a partially permeable membrane that allows the passage of water molecules but not solute molecules'

PURE H_2O SUGAR + H_2O

HIGH CONC^n OF WATER   LOW CONC^n OF WATER

- Remember the two classic experiments with dialysis tubing and 'chips'.

ACTIVE TRANSPORT requires energy to absorb ions against a concentration gradient ie. from a more concentrated to a less concentrated solution.

NITRATE IONS

SPECIALISED EXCHANGE SURFACES

Many organ systems are SPECIALISED FOR EXCHANGING MATERIALS.

EXAMPLES IN HUMANS

1. The alveoli in the lungs provide a MASSIVE SURFACE AREA for EXCHANGE OF OXYGEN AND CARBON DIOXIDE.

2. The villi in the small intestine provide a MASSIVE SURFACE AREA for ABSORPTION OF PRODUCTS OF DIGESTION.

EXAMPLES IN PLANTS

1. The root hair cells in the roots provide a MASSIVE SURFACE AREA for ABSORPTION OF WATER AND MINERAL IONS.

2. The flattened shape and internal air spaces in the leaf provide a MASSIVE SURFACE AREA for EXCHANGE OF OXYGEN AND CARBON DIOXIDE.

CARBON DIOXIDE   OXYGEN

PHOTOSYNTHESIS AND PLANT MINERAL REQUIREMENTS

$$\text{CARBON DIOXIDE} + \text{WATER} \xrightarrow[\text{Chlorophyll}]{\text{Light}} \text{GLUCOSE} + \text{OXYGEN}$$

The glucose provides energy via respiration which is used to ...
- CONVERT SUGARS INTO STARCH
- CONVERT SUGARS INTO CELLULOSE for cell walls
- CONVERT SUGARS AND NITRATES INTO AMINO ACIDS for proteins
- CONVERT SUGARS INTO LIPIDS (fats or oils) for storage in seeds

FACTORS AFFECTING PHOTOSYNTHESIS

TEMPERATURE CO_2 CONCENTRATION *[1]   LIGHT INTENSITY *[2]

*[1] At this point, sunlight or temperature must be limiting factor.
*[2] At this point, carbon dioxide or temperature must be limiting factor.

MINERAL REQUIREMENTS

Lack of NITRATES, leads to stunted growth and yellow older leaves.

POTASSIUM needed for enzymes ... yellow leaves with dead spots.

PHOSPHATES for respiration and photosynthesis ... poor root growth and purple younger leaves.

TRANSPIRATION

THE LEAF

- Water is lost via stomata. Waxy cuticle prevents water loss from upper surface. This is thicker for plants which live in HOT, DRY or WINDY conditions.

STOMATA

THE STEM

① Evaporation via stomata.
② Water from the xylem to leaf via osmosis ...
③ 'Thread' of water in xylem pulled upwards.
④ Water enters xylem from roots.
⑤ Water enters root hair cells via osmosis to replace water which has entered the xylem.

H_2O CO_2 CO_2 H_2O

PHLOEM XYLEM

SUGARS   SOLUBLE MINERAL SALTS   WATER

THE ROOT

- Water enters the root by OSMOSIS. The surface area is increased by the presence of root hairs.

SUPPORTING PLANTS AND HORMONES

'CONTROLLING WATER LOSS ... stomata stay open to allow diffusion of gases in photosynthesis but if there is insufficient water the guard cells become flaccid and the stomata close'.

Plant cells become rigid when they are full of water. This is the main method of support in non-woody plants.

H_2O Water passes into the cells by osmosis if they are in a less concentrated solution. H_2O

This causes TURGOR PRESSURE which causes the cells to become rigid. Maintenance of turgor provides support.

HORMONES

In shoots growth is stimulated.

In roots growth is retarded.

LIGHT

Light causes hormones to accumulate on the shaded part of the stem.

Hormones can be used artificially as ROOTING COMPOUNDS, RIPENING HORMONE and SELECTIVE WEEDKILLERS.

SUMMARY QUESTIONS

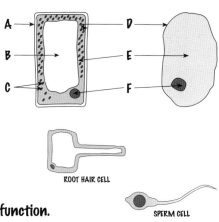

ROOT HAIR CELL

SPERM CELL

1. a) Label the cells opposite.
   b) List the three structures they have in common and explain what their functions are.

2. What role do mitochondria play in the release of energy within cells?

3. a) What is meant by a specialised cell?
   b) Explain how a root hair cell is well adapted to its function.
   c) Explain how a sperm cell is well adapted to its function.
   d) Describe another specialised cell and explain how it is adapted to its function.

4. Rearrange the following into the correct order starting with the least complex and ending with the most complex. ORGAN SYSTEMS - TISSUES - ORGANISM - CELLS - ORGANS.

5. a) Label the substances which are moving into and out of the amoeba in the diagram below.
   b) Which process causes them to move in this way?
   c) Draw diagrams to show how this process can be demonstrated in the laboratory.
   d) Give an example of this process occurring in plants. Describe fully what happens.
   e) Explain why this process occurs.

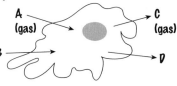

6. a) Explain what is meant by the word osmosis.
   b) Explain what would happen in the following experiments.

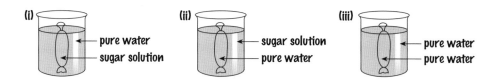

7. a) Explain the difference between diffusion and osmosis.
   b) State whether the following are examples of diffusion or osmosis ...
      i) Carbon dioxide entering a leaf.
      ii) Water vapour leaving a leaf.
      iii) Water passing from one leaf cell into another.
      iv) Oxygen passing from the alveoli into the blood.
      v) Water passing from the soil into a root hair cell.

8. Explain how a root hair cell can absorb ions from the soil against a concentration gradient.

9. What do all specialised exchange surfaces have in common?

10. a) Explain how a specialised exchange surface is achieved in the lungs.
    b) Explain how a specialised exchange surface is achieved in the small intestine.
    c) Explain how a specialised exchange surface is achieved in the root hair cells.
    d) Explain how a specialised exchange surface is achieved in the leaves.

11. a) Besides carbon dioxide, which other three things do plants need in order to make their own food?

    b) How does carbon dioxide actually get into the plant?

    c) At point 'A' on the graph opposite, which factor is no longer limiting the rate of photosynthesis?

    d) The carbohydrate produced in this process is soluble, but may be changed into an insoluble carbohydrate for storage. What is the name of this insoluble storage compound?

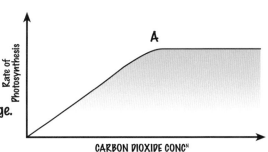

12. The carbohydrate produced in photosynthesis can be used immediately by a plant to provide energy via respiration. Some of this energy is used to build up smaller molecules into larger ones. Give three examples of this.

13. Which minerals are the following plants short of?

    a) The plant has stunted growth and yellow older leaves.

    b) The plant has yellow leaves with dead spots.

    c) The plant has poor root growth and purple younger leaves.

14. a) What is transpiration and why does it occur?

    b) How are plants which live in hot, dry conditions adapted to prevent too much water loss from their leaves?

    c) Describe the different functions carried out by the plant's two transport systems.

15. a) What are stomata?

    b) What role do they play in increasing or decreasing the rate of transpiration?

    c) If transpiration were to stop completely, what effect would this have on photosynthesis?

16. a) Explain as fully as you can how water moves into plant cells.

    b) What prevents plant cells from absorbing too much water and bursting?

    c) Explain why plants wilt if there is insufficient water in the soil.

17. a) Explain how hormones control the direction of growth of shoots.

    b) Explain how hormones control the direction of growth of roots.

    c) What would happen to the shoot in the diagram if it was illuminated from just one side for 3 or 4 days?

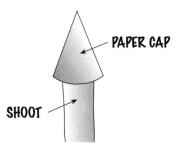

18. Describe the ways in which hormones can be used artificially in agriculture.

The DIGESTIVE SYSTEM is really made up of a long MUSCULAR TUBE in which ENZYMES speed up (catalyse) the breakdown of LARGE INSOLUBLE MOLECULES eg. starch, proteins and fats into SMALLER SOLUBLE MOLECULES so that they can pass through the walls of the small intestine and into the bloodstream. Reabsorption of water takes place in the large intestine leaving indigestible food which leaves the body as faeces via the anus.

The Human Digestive System

GULLET

SALIVARY GLANDS
Produce the enzyme
AMYLASE.

LIVER
Produces BILE which
helps in fat digestion.

GALL BLADDER

LARGE INTESTINE (COLON)
Excess water, from the contents
of the intestines, is REABSORBED
into the blood here.

ANUS
The remaining indigestible
food makes up the faeces
which leave the body here.

STOMACH
Produces the enzyme
PROTEASE,
and also hydrochloric acid
which kills bacteria, and
also provides the ideal
conditions for protease.

PANCREAS
Produces all three enzymes ...
AMYLASE,
PROTEASE and
LIPASE.

SMALL INTESTINE (ILEUM)
Produces all three enzymes
AMYLASE,
PROTEASE and
LIPASE.
Also, small soluble molecules
are ABSORBED INTO THE
BLOODSTREAM.

The Function Of Bile

LIVER

GALL
BLADDER

SMALL INTESTINE

Bile is produced in the LIVER and then stored in the GALL BLADDER ...
... before being released into the SMALL INTESTINE.
Bile has 2 functions ...

1 ... it neutralises the acid, which was added to food in the stomach, to produce ALKALINE conditions in which the enzymes of the small intestine work best.

2 ... it EMULSIFIES fats ie. it breaks large drops of fat into small droplets to increase their surface area. This enables the lipase enzymes to work much faster.

GLOBULES
OF FAT

 BILE

DROPLETS OF FAT

Enzyme Summary

Three enzymes PROTEASE, LIPASE and AMYLASE are produced in four separate regions of the digestive system. They digest Proteins, Fats and Carbohydrates to produce molecules which can be absorbed.

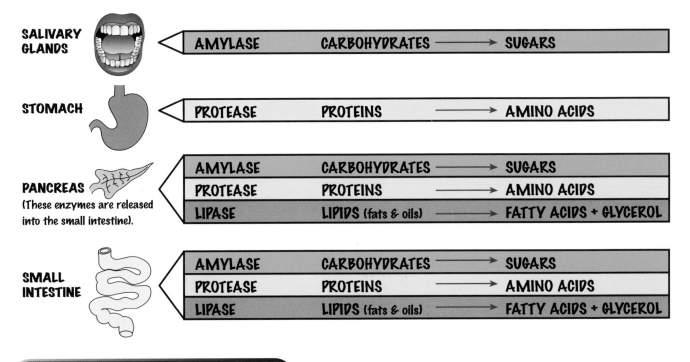

SALIVARY GLANDS

| AMYLASE | CARBOHYDRATES ⟶ SUGARS |

STOMACH

| PROTEASE | PROTEINS ⟶ AMINO ACIDS |

PANCREAS
(These enzymes are released into the small intestine).

AMYLASE	CARBOHYDRATES ⟶ SUGARS
PROTEASE	PROTEINS ⟶ AMINO ACIDS
LIPASE	LIPIDS (fats & oils) ⟶ FATTY ACIDS + GLYCEROL

SMALL INTESTINE

AMYLASE	CARBOHYDRATES ⟶ SUGARS
PROTEASE	PROTEINS ⟶ AMINO ACIDS
LIPASE	LIPIDS (fats & oils) ⟶ FATTY ACIDS + GLYCEROL

Absorption In The Small Intestine

The three enzymes catalyse the breakdown of LARGE INSOLUBLE MOLECULES into SMALL SOLUBLE MOLECULES which then diffuse through the walls of the small intestine into the bloodstream.

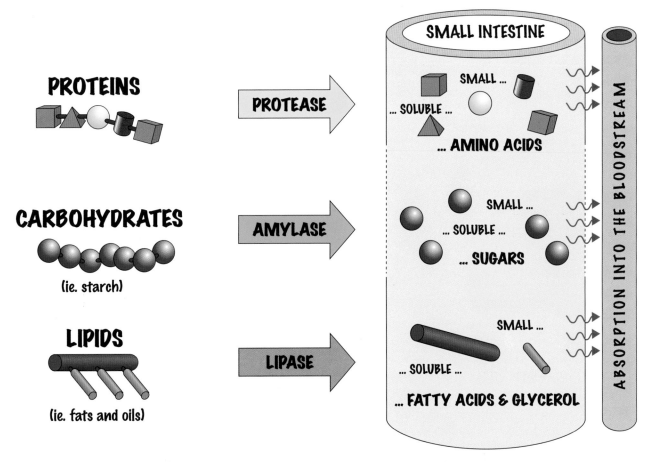

PROTEINS

PROTEASE

CARBOHYDRATES
(ie. starch)

AMYLASE

LIPIDS
(ie. fats and oils)

LIPASE

SMALL INTESTINE

SMALL ... ... SOLUBLE ... ... AMINO ACIDS

SMALL ... ... SOLUBLE ... ... SUGARS

SMALL ... ... SOLUBLE ... ... FATTY ACIDS & GLYCEROL

ABSORPTION INTO THE BLOODSTREAM

The Function Of The Circulatory System

The circulatory system is the body's transport system.
- It carries blood from the heart to all the cells of the body ...
- ... to provide them with FOOD and OXYGEN, and ...
- ... carries WASTE PRODUCTS including CARBON DIOXIDE away from the cells.
- Blood is pumped to the lungs so that CARBON DIOXIDE can be exchanged for OXYGEN.
- The system consists of THE HEART, THE BLOOD VESSELS, and THE BLOOD.

LUNGS

(R) (L)

HEART

BODY

■ = DEOXYGENATED
■ = OXYGENATED

The Heart And Major Blood Vessels

The heart acts as a PUMP in a DOUBLE CIRCULATORY SYSTEM.

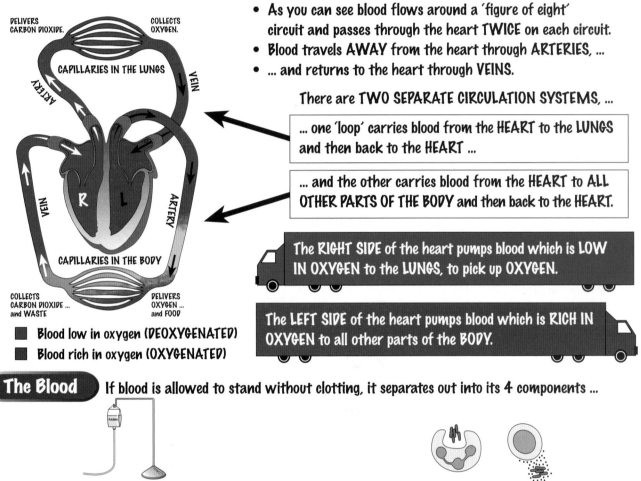

DELIVERS CARBON DIOXIDE.
COLLECTS OXYGEN.

CAPILLARIES IN THE LUNGS

ARTERY   VEIN

VEIN   ARTERY

R   L

CAPILLARIES IN THE BODY

COLLECTS CARBON DIOXIDE ... and WASTE
DELIVERS OXYGEN ... and FOOD

- As you can see blood flows around a 'figure of eight' circuit and passes through the heart TWICE on each circuit.
- Blood travels AWAY from the heart through ARTERIES, ...
- ... and returns to the heart through VEINS.

There are TWO SEPARATE CIRCULATION SYSTEMS, ...

> ... one 'loop' carries blood from the HEART to the LUNGS and then back to the HEART ...

> ... and the other carries blood from the HEART to ALL OTHER PARTS OF THE BODY and then back to the HEART.

The RIGHT SIDE of the heart pumps blood which is LOW IN OXYGEN to the LUNGS, to pick up OXYGEN.

The LEFT SIDE of the heart pumps blood which is RICH IN OXYGEN to all other parts of the BODY.

■ Blood low in oxygen (DEOXYGENATED)
■ Blood rich in oxygen (OXYGENATED)

The Blood

If blood is allowed to stand without clotting, it separates out into its 4 components ...

PLASMA is a straw-coloured liquid which transports ...
- ... carbon dioxide from the organs to the lungs ...
- ... soluble products of digestion from the small intestine to the organs ...
- ... other wastes (eg. urea) from the liver to the kidneys.

WHITE CELLS have a nucleus which is variable in shape.
- Some engulf invading microbes to defend the body ...
- ... while others produce ANTIBODIES to attack them.
- There's 1 white cell for every 600 red cells!!

RED CELLS transport OXYGEN from the lungs to the organs.

PLATELETS are tiny pieces of cell which have no nucleus.
- They clump together when a blood vessel is damaged ...
- ... and form a meshwork of fibres to produce a CLOT.

------ HIGHER TIER ------
- They have NO NUCLEUS so that they can contain lots of HAEMOGLOBIN, (a red pigment which can carry oxygen).
- In the lungs HAEMOGLOBIN combines with oxygen to form OXYHAEMOGLOBIN. In other organs OXYHAEMOGLOBIN splits up into HAEMOGLOBIN plus OXYGEN.

The Heart In More Detail

The HEART is a muscular organ in the circulatory system and PUMPS BLOOD around the body.

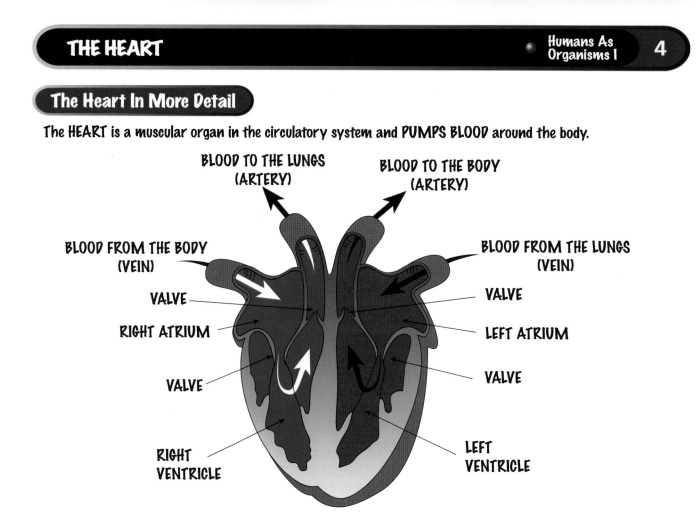

BLOOD TO THE LUNGS (ARTERY)

BLOOD TO THE BODY (ARTERY)

BLOOD FROM THE BODY (VEIN)

BLOOD FROM THE LUNGS (VEIN)

VALVE

VALVE

RIGHT ATRIUM

LEFT ATRIUM

VALVE

VALVE

RIGHT VENTRICLE

LEFT VENTRICLE

- Most of the wall of the heart is made of MUSCLE.
- ATRIA are the smaller, LESS MUSCULAR upper chambers, which receive blood coming back to the heart through VEINS.
- VENTRICLES are the larger, MORE MUSCULAR lower chambers.
  The LEFT is more muscular than the right since it has to pump blood around the whole body.
- VALVES make sure that the blood flows in the right direction, and can't flow backwards.

How The Heart Pumps Blood

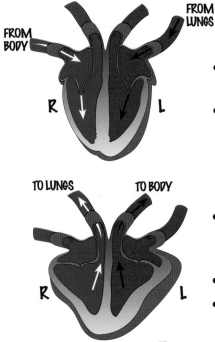

FROM LUNGS

FROM BODY

R   L

- When the HEART MUSCLE RELAXES, blood flows into the ATRIA, through veins, from the LUNGS and the rest of the BODY.
- The ATRIA then CONTRACT squeezing blood into the VENTRICLES.

TO LUNGS   TO BODY

R   L

- When the VENTRICLES CONTRACT (squeeze) ...
  ... blood is forced out of the lower chambers into two arteries ...
  ... these carry blood to the body and the lungs.
- The blood can't flow backwards because of VALVES in the heart.
- The heart muscle now relaxes and the whole process starts again.

There are three types of blood vessels ... ARTERIES, VEINS and CAPILLARIES.
They form the 'plumbing' of the circulatory system.

Arteries

- Thick wall containing ELASTIC and MUSCLE fibres to cope with the much higher pressure in these vessels.
- Much smaller lumen compared to the thickness of the wall.
- No valves.
- Carry blood AWAY from the heart.
- Substances from the blood CANNOT pass through the artery walls.

Veins

- Thinner wall containing LESS ELASTIC and MUSCLE fibres.
- Much bigger lumen compared to the thickness of the wall.
- Have VALVES to prevent backflow of blood.
- Carry blood TOWARDS the heart.
- Substances CANNOT pass through the veins' walls.

VALVE

Capillaries

- Narrow, thin-walled vessels, just ONE CELL THICK.
- Microscopic (too small to see without a microscope).
- EXCHANGE OF SUBSTANCES between cells and blood ONLY takes place here.
- Connect arteries to veins.

Exchange Of Substances At The Capillaries

Arteries branch into tiny one cell thick capillaries which pass close to each cell before reuniting to form a vein.

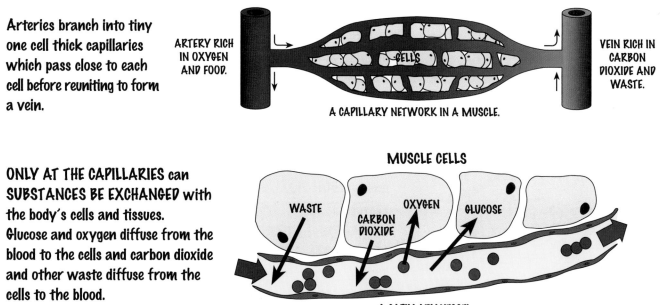

ARTERY RICH IN OXYGEN AND FOOD.

CELLS

VEIN RICH IN CARBON DIOXIDE AND WASTE.

A CAPILLARY NETWORK IN A MUSCLE.

ONLY AT THE CAPILLARIES can SUBSTANCES BE EXCHANGED with the body's cells and tissues. Glucose and oxygen diffuse from the blood to the cells and carbon dioxide and other waste diffuse from the cells to the blood.

MUSCLE CELLS

WASTE   CARBON DIOXIDE   OXYGEN   GLUCOSE

A CAPILLARY VESSEL
(one cell thick)

The Breathing System

The most important structures in the breathing system are shown in the diagram below ...

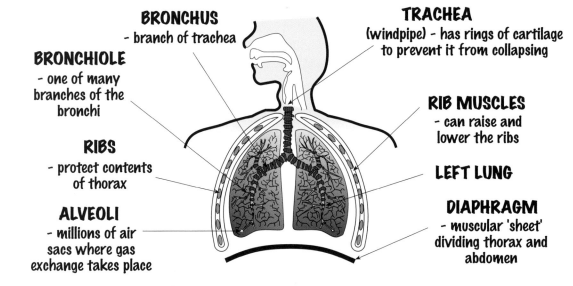

BRONCHUS
- branch of trachea

TRACHEA
(windpipe) - has rings of cartilage to prevent it from collapsing

BRONCHIOLE
- one of many branches of the bronchi

RIB MUSCLES
- can raise and lower the ribs

RIBS
- protect contents of thorax

LEFT LUNG

ALVEOLI
- millions of air sacs where gas exchange takes place

DIAPHRAGM
- muscular 'sheet' dividing thorax and abdomen

- The RIBCAGE protects the contents of the THORAX ie. the HEART and LUNGS.

Diffusion Of Oxygen And Carbon Dioxide In The Alveoli

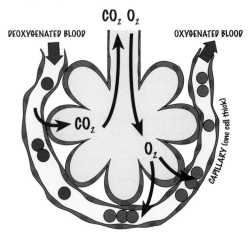

CO_2 O_2

DEOXYGENATED BLOOD

OXYGENATED BLOOD

CO_2

O_2

CAPILLARY (one cell thick)

A SINGLE ALVEOLUS AND A CAPILLARY.

- The TRACHEA divides into two tubes ...
- ... called the BRONCHI, which divide again, several times, ...
- ... to form the BRONCHIOLES which continue to divide ...
- ... until they end as air sacs called ALVEOLI (there are millions of these) ...
- ... which are very close to the blood CAPILLARIES.

and here, ...
- ... CARBON DIOXIDE diffuses from the BLOOD into the ALVEOLI.
- ... OXYGEN diffuses from the ALVEOLI into the blood.

This means the blood has swapped its CARBON DIOXIDE for OXYGEN and is now OXYGENATED.

HIGHER TIER

Features Which Make The Lungs An Excellent Exchange Surface

ALVEOLI

The arrangement of alveoli and capillaries in the lungs makes the lungs very EFFICIENT at exchanging OXYGEN and CARBON DIOXIDE,
because ...
- ... they have a LARGE, MOIST SURFACE AREA.
- ... they have an EXCELLENT CAPILLARY BLOOD SUPPLY.

Inhaling

In order to take air into the lungs, we have to increase the volume of the thorax.

This happens in two ways ...

- ... the ribcage moves out (upwards and outwards really!), and ...
- ... the diaphragm becomes flatter.

THIS MAKES THE VOLUME OF THE THORAX, AND THEREFORE THE INTERNAL LUNG VOLUME BIGGER, AND AIR ENTERS THE LUNGS.

INCREASE IN VOLUME — RIBCAGE RAISED — RIBS — DIAPHRAGM FLATTENS

Exhaling

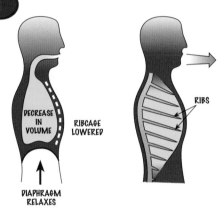

In order to make air move out of the lungs, we have to decrease the volume of the thorax.

This happens in two ways ...

- ... the ribcage moves in (downwards and inwards really!), and ...
- ... the diaphragm goes back to its relaxed position.

THIS MAKES THE VOLUME OF THE THORAX, AND THEREFORE THE INTERNAL LUNG VOLUME SMALLER, AND AIR LEAVES THE LUNGS.

DECREASE IN VOLUME — RIBCAGE LOWERED — RIBS — DIAPHRAGM RELAXES

HIGHER TIER

Ventilation In Terms Of Pressure Differences

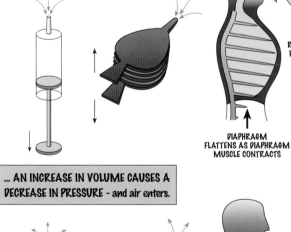

It's the same principle with the SYRINGE and the BELLOWS ...

... AN INCREASE IN VOLUME CAUSES A DECREASE IN PRESSURE - and air enters.

RIBCAGE RAISED

DIAPHRAGM FLATTENS AS DIAPHRAGM MUSCLE CONTRACTS

To inhale:

- The muscles between the ribs contract, pulling the ribcage upwards and outwards.
- At the same time the diaphragm muscles contract causing the diaphragm to flatten.
- These two movements cause an increase in the volume of the thorax ...
- ... and therefore a decrease in pressure which results in atmospheric air entering.

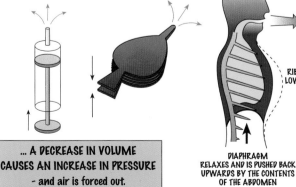

... A DECREASE IN VOLUME CAUSES AN INCREASE IN PRESSURE - and air is forced out.

RIBCAGE LOWERED

DIAPHRAGM RELAXES AND IS PUSHED BACK UPWARDS BY THE CONTENTS OF THE ABDOMEN

To exhale:

- The muscles between the ribs relax allowing them to fall.
- The diaphragm muscles also relax.
- These movements cause a decrease in the volume of the thorax ...
- ... and therefore an increase in pressure resulting in air being forced out.

Aerobic Respiration ... 'is the release of energy from the breakdown of glucose, ...
... by combining it with OXYGEN inside living cells.'
(The energy is actually contained inside the glucose molecule.)

THE EQUATION: GLUCOSE + OXYGEN ⟹ CARBON DIOXIDE + WATER + ENERGY

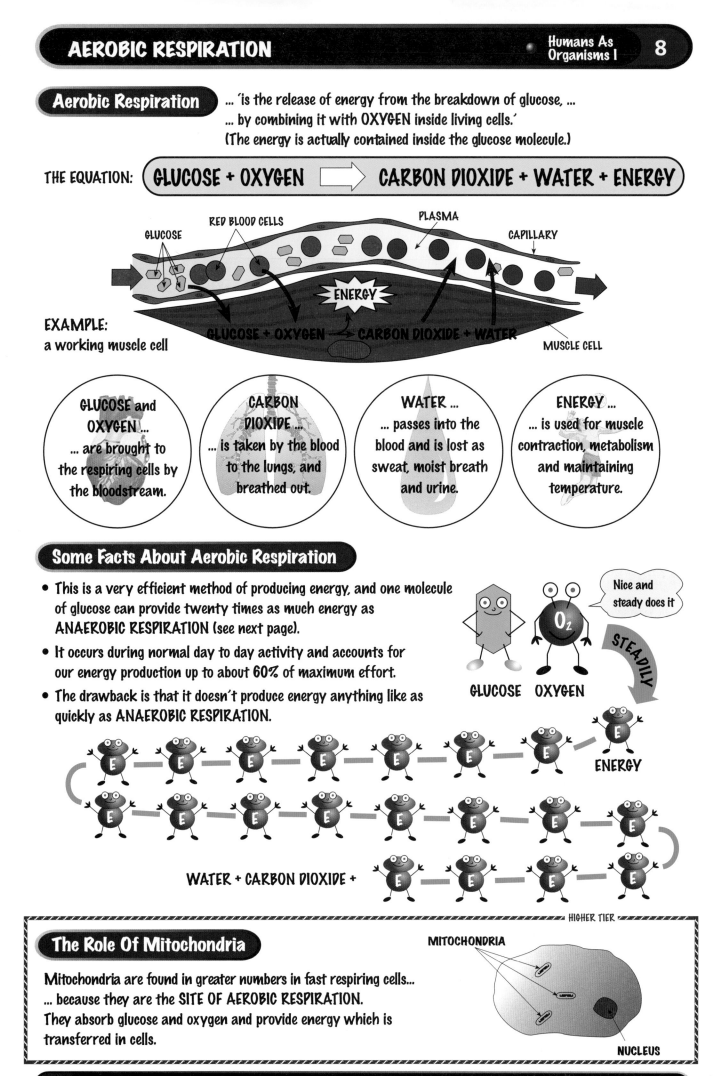

EXAMPLE:
a working muscle cell

GLUCOSE and OXYGEN ...
... are brought to the respiring cells by the bloodstream.

CARBON DIOXIDE ...
... is taken by the blood to the lungs, and breathed out.

WATER ...
... passes into the blood and is lost as sweat, moist breath and urine.

ENERGY ...
... is used for muscle contraction, metabolism and maintaining temperature.

Some Facts About Aerobic Respiration

- This is a very efficient method of producing energy, and one molecule of glucose can provide twenty times as much energy as ANAEROBIC RESPIRATION (see next page).

- It occurs during normal day to day activity and accounts for our energy production up to about 60% of maximum effort.

- The drawback is that it doesn't produce energy anything like as quickly as ANAEROBIC RESPIRATION.

Nice and steady does it

GLUCOSE   OXYGEN   STEADILY

ENERGY

WATER + CARBON DIOXIDE +

━━━━━━━━━━━ HIGHER TIER ━━━━━━━━━━━

The Role Of Mitochondria

MITOCHONDRIA

Mitochondria are found in greater numbers in fast respiring cells...
... because they are the SITE OF AEROBIC RESPIRATION.
They absorb glucose and oxygen and provide energy which is transferred in cells.

NUCLEUS

Anaerobic Respiration

... is the release of a little bit of energy, <u>very quickly</u>, inside living cells, from the INCOMPLETE breakdown of glucose in the ABSENCE OF OXYGEN.

THE EQUATION: **GLUCOSE ⟹ LACTIC ACID + A BIT OF ENERGY**

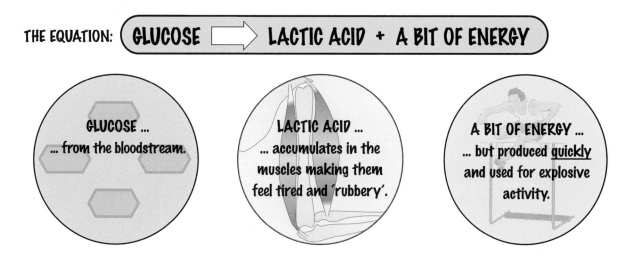

GLUCOSE ...
... from the bloodstream.

LACTIC ACID ...
... accumulates in the muscles making them feel tired and 'rubbery'.

A BIT OF ENERGY ...
... but produced <u>quickly</u> and used for explosive activity.

- This happens when the muscles are working so hard that...
- ...the lungs and bloodstream can't deliver enough OXYGEN, to respire the available glucose aerobically.
- The waste product from this process is LACTIC ACID, and this accumulates in the tissues.
- After exercise the body needs oxygen to break down the lactic acid, and the oxygen that is needed is called an OXYGEN DEBT.

--- HIGHER TIER ---

Some Facts About Anaerobic Respiration

- Because anaerobic respiration involves the <u>incomplete</u> breakdown of glucose, much less energy is released, than in aerobic respiration (about $\frac{1}{20}$ th in fact!).
- However it can produce energy much faster over a short period of time, until fatigue sets in.
- When the muscles are fatigued, they stop contracting efficiently and deep breathing is required to 'repay the oxygen debt' by oxidising lactic acid to carbon dioxide and water.

GLUCOSE

EXPLOSIVELY

E ENERGY

+

LACTIC ACID

What Cells Do With Their Energy

The energy released during respiration is used in the following ways ...

- To build larger **MOLECULES** using smaller ones.
- To enable **MUSCLES** to contract.
- To **MAINTAIN TEMPERATURE** in colder surroundings.

They all begin with **M**.
(Remember the 'M's')

--- HIGHER TIER ---

- To actively transport materials across **MEMBRANES.**

DIGESTIVE SYSTEM, ENZYMES AND ABSORPTION

Enzymes breakdown large molecules into smaller soluble molecules.

SALIVARY GLANDS — AMYLASE.
GULLET
STOMACH — PROTEASE
LIVER
PANCREAS — AMYLASE, PROTEASE, LIPASE.
GALL BLADDER
LARGE INTESTINE
SMALL INTESTINE — AMYLASE, PROTEASE, LIPASE.
ANUS

LIVER
SMALL INTESTINE

Bile produced in the liver, neutralises acid and emulsifies fats.

SALIVARY GLANDS	AMYLASE	CARBOHYDRATES → SUGARS	
STOMACH	PROTEASE	PROTEINS → AMINO ACIDS	
PANCREAS	AMYLASE	CARBOHYDRATES → SUGARS	
	PROTEASE	PROTEINS → AMINO ACIDS	
	LIPASE	LIPIDS (fats & oils) → FATTY ACIDS + GLYCEROL	
SMALL INTESTINE	AMYLASE	CARBOHYDRATES → SUGARS	
	PROTEASE	PROTEINS → AMINO ACIDS	
	LIPASE	LIPIDS (fats & oils) → FATTY ACIDS + GLYCEROL	

The products of digestion are absorbed into the bloodstream in the small intestine.

ABSORPTION IN THE SMALL INTESTINE

SMALL INTESTINE

PROTEINS → PROTEASE → ... AMINO ACIDS

CARBOHYDRATES (ie. starch) → AMYLASE → ... SUGARS

LIPIDS (ie. fats and oils) → LIPASE → ... FATTY ACIDS & GLYCEROL

ABSORPTION INTO THE BLOODSTREAM

CIRCULATION

LUNGS
ARTERY
VEIN
RIGHT ATRIUM
LEFT ATRIUM
RIGHT VENTRICLE
LEFT VENTRICLE
VEIN
ARTERY
BODY

• There are valves between each atrium and ventricle to prevent backflow of blood.

■ OXYGENATED BLOOD
■ DEOXYGENATED BLOOD

• Arteries transport blood away from the heart.
• Veins transport blood to the heart.

PLASMA carries CO_2, glucose, urea.

WHITE CELLS defence system.

PLATELETS help blood to clot.

RED CELLS transport oxygen from the lungs to the organs.

ARTERIES
Thick wall, no valves, carry blood away from heart.

They have no nucleus so they can contain more haemoglobin. This combines reversibly with oxygen to form OXYHAEMOGLOBIN.

VEINS
Thinner walls, valves, carry blood back to heart.

CAPILLARIES
One cell thick so exchange can occur.

• Substances diffuse into and out of the blood. Diffusion is a net movement of particles from an area of high concentration to an area of low concentration.

BREATHING

BRONCHUS
TRACHEA
BRONCHIOLE
RIB MUSCLES
RIBS
ALVEOLI
LEFT LUNG
DIAPHRAGM

CO_2 O_2

CO_2
O_2

In the alveoli, CO_2 diffuses from the blood into the lungs and O_2 diffuses from the lungs into the blood. The blood becomes oxygenated.

VENTILATION
Air moves into the lungs when the ribcage moves outwards and the diaphragm becomes flatter. The opposite happens when we breathe out.

The alveoli are an excellent exchange surface because they have ...
• A LARGE, MOIST SURFACE AREA.
• AN EXCELLENT BLOOD SUPPLY.

INHALING
Rib muscles and diaphragm contract causing an increase in the volume of the thorax. This causes a decrease in pressure inside the thorax and atmospheric air enters.

RIBCAGE RAISED

DIAPHRAGM FLATTENS AS DIAPHRAGM MUSCLE CONTRACTS

EXHALING
Rib muscles and diaphragm relax causing a decrease in the volume of the thorax. This causes an increase in pressure inside the thorax and air is forced out.

• Cartilage keeps the airways open.

RIBCAGE LOWERED

DIAPHRAGM RELAXES

AEROBIC AND ANAEROBIC RESPIRATION

AEROBIC RESPIRATION

GLUCOSE + OXYGEN → CARBON DIOXIDE + WATER + ENERGY

This is the release of energy from the breakdown of glucose, by combining it with oxygen inside living cells. This provides lots of energy very efficiently, although fairly steadily. (Occurs in Mitochondria)

Nice and steady does it
STEADILY
GLUCOSE OXYGEN
ENERGY

WATER + CARBON DIOXIDE +

ANAEROBIC RESPIRATION

GLUCOSE → LACTIC ACID + A BIT OF ENERGY

Occurs when muscles are working very hard and can operate only for a short time due to build up of lactic acid as a waste product. This needs oxygen to break it down ie. OXYGEN DEBT. Produces energy quickly - but not much of it. Ideal for 'explosive' activity.

EXPLOSIVELY
GLUCOSE
ENERGY
+
LACTIC ACID

After a while fatigue sets in and muscles stop contracting efficiently. The oxygen needed after exercise is used to oxidise lactic acid to carbon dioxide and water.

• Cells use energy ...
... to build large MOLECULES
... for MUSCLE contraction
... to MAINTAIN temperature
... to move materials across MEMBRANES (ACTIVELY)

'The 4M's'

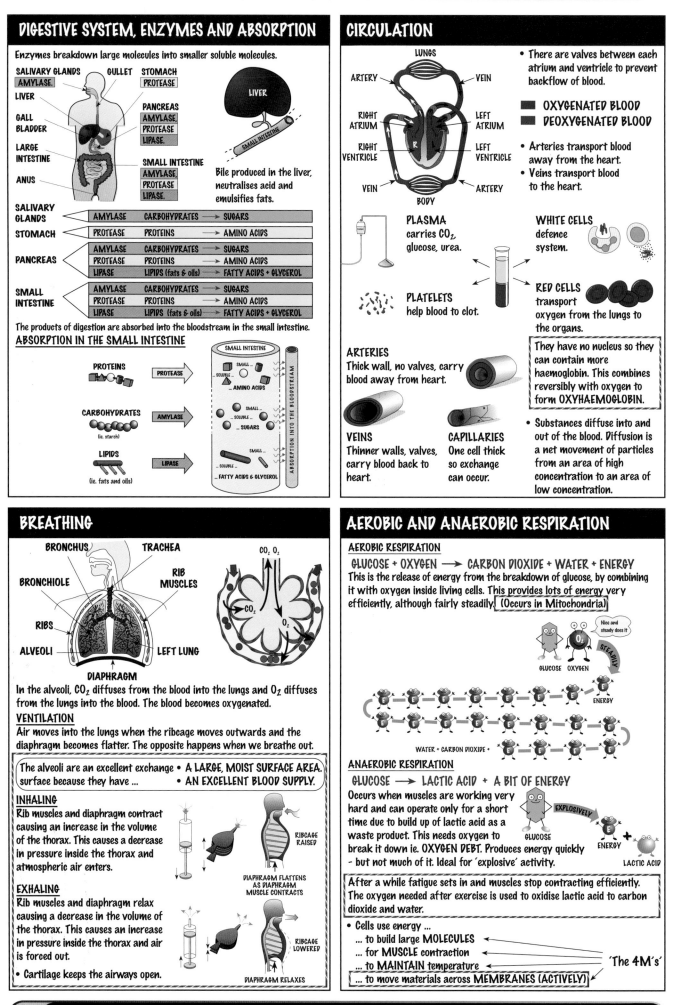

1. a) Label the diagram of the human digestive system.
   b) What is the purpose of the digestive system?
   c) In which organ does reabsorption of water take place?

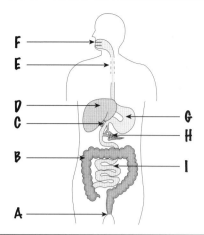

2. The liver produces bile which is stored in the gall bladder prior to being used in digestion. State two functions of bile.

3. Complete the table below for the stomach, pancreas and small intestine.

REGION	ENZYME PRODUCED	FOOD SUBSTANCE ACTED ON	PRODUCTS FORMED
MOUTH	AMYLASE	CARBOHYDRATES	SUGARS

4. a) What is the function of the circulatory system?
   b) Draw a simple diagram to show the movement of blood between the heart, lungs and body.
      On your diagram label the deoxygenated and the oxygenated blood.
   c) Which blood vessels carry blood away from the heart?
   d) Which blood vessels carry blood towards the heart?

5. a) What are the four components that make up blood?
   b) Which component is responsible for the production of clots?
   c) Which component is responsible for the production of antibodies?
   d) Which component transports oxygen from the lungs to the organs?
   e) Which component transports urea from the liver to the kidneys?

6. a) Why is the absence of a nucleus in a red blood cell an example of an adaptation to function?
   b) Write down the chemical changes which take place when a red blood cell is ...
      i) in the lungs ii) in a capillary close to body cells.

7. Using the words RIGHT ATRIUM, LEFT ATRIUM, RIGHT VENTRICLE, LEFT VENTRICLE, ARTERY, VEIN, CAPILLARIES IN THE BODY, CAPILLARIES IN THE LUNGS, as many times as you wish, describe the journey of a red blood cell around the circulatory system. (Start the journey at the left ventricle.)

8. a) What are atria?
   b) What are ventricles?
   c) Why does the heart contain valves?

9. Why is the wall of an artery much thicker than the wall of a vein?

10. a) Which substances are carried to and from cells by capillaries?
    b) Draw the structure of a capillary and briefly state how it differs from ...
       i) an artery and ii) a vein.

11. a) Label the diagram of the lungs opposite.
    b) Which structure ...
       i) has rings of cartilage to prevent it from collapsing?
       ii) protects the contents of the thorax?
       iii) raises and lowers the ribs?
       iv) is a muscular 'sheet' that divides the thorax and abdomen?

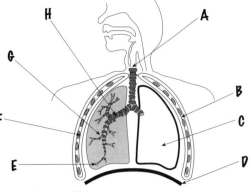

12. What is the purpose of the ribcage?

13. Describe the exchange process that takes place between an alveolus and a capillary.

14. a) What happens to the ribcage and diaphragm when air is inhaled?
    b) What consequence is there then for the thorax and the lungs?
    c) What happens to the ribcage and diaphragm when air is exhaled?
    d) What consequence is there then for the thorax and the lungs?

15. a) Explain how air is inhaled into the lungs. Use the words: DIAPHRAGM, RIBCAGE, RIB MUSCLES, THORAX VOLUME and THORAX PRESSURE in your explanation.
    b) Describe how the arrangement of the alveoli and capillaries make the lungs well-adapted for their role as a specialised exchange surface.

16. a) What is aerobic respiration?
    b) Write down a word equation for aerobic respiration.
    c) What is anaerobic respiration?
    d) Write down a word equation for anaerobic respiration.
    e) Which of the above forms of respiration is the most efficient? Explain your answer.

17. What role do mitochondria play in aerobic respiration?

18. A sprinter completes a 100m race during which his heart rate was monitored.
    The table below shows the data which was recorded.

TIME AFTER START (s)	0	1	2	3	4	5	6	7	8	9	10	11
HEART RATE beats/min	75	95	105	110	125	130	135	140	145	150	155	160

    a) Draw a graph using this data.
    b) Explain why his heart rate should change in this way in response to hard physical exercise.
    c) During the first part of the sprint the athlete's muscles would be producing energy by respiring aerobically. Explain why.
    d) Towards the latter part of the race anaerobic respiration would start to take place. Explain why.
    e) What effect would this anaerobic respiration have on the athlete at the end of the race?

19. In what ways is the energy released during respiration used?

Components Of The Nervous System

- The nervous system consists of the BRAIN, the SPINAL CORD, the SPINAL NERVES and RECEPTORS.
- It allows organisms to REACT TO THEIR SURROUNDINGS and ...
      ... to COORDINATE THEIR BEHAVIOUR.
- The FIVE SENSES, namely SEEING, HEARING, TASTING, SMELLING and TOUCHING play a very important part in these processes, in which information from receptors passes along neurones to the brain which coordinates the response.

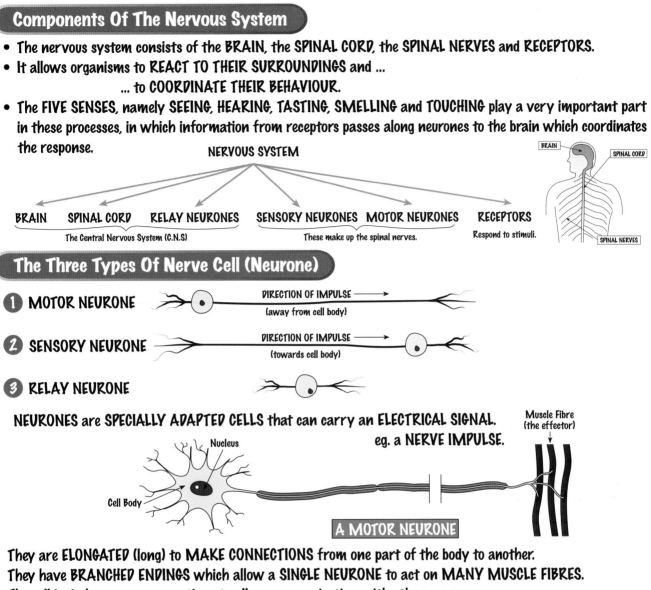

The Three Types Of Nerve Cell (Neurone)

1 MOTOR NEURONE   DIRECTION OF IMPULSE ⟶ (away from cell body)

2 SENSORY NEURONE   DIRECTION OF IMPULSE ⟶ (towards cell body)

3 RELAY NEURONE

NEURONES are SPECIALLY ADAPTED CELLS that can carry an ELECTRICAL SIGNAL. eg. a NERVE IMPULSE.

Muscle Fibre (the effector)

Nucleus

Cell Body

A MOTOR NEURONE

They are ELONGATED (long) to MAKE CONNECTIONS from one part of the body to another.
They have BRANCHED ENDINGS which allow a SINGLE NEURONE to act on MANY MUSCLE FIBRES.
The cell body has many connections to allow communication with other neurones.

Reflex Action

Some responses to stimuli are designed to prevent injury to the body. When certain receptors are stimulated they cause a very fast, automatic response to the presence of danger. These are called simple reflexes and involve both sensory and motor neurones. The basic pathway for a simple reflex is shown below ...

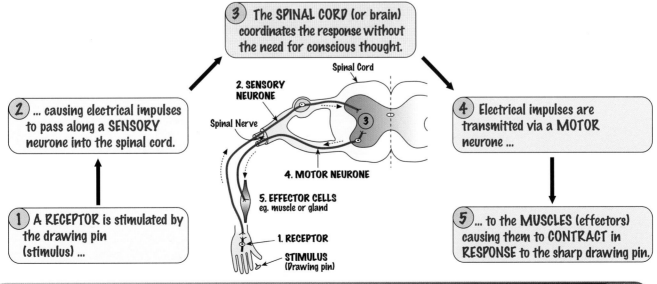

3 The SPINAL CORD (or brain) coordinates the response without the need for conscious thought.

2 ... causing electrical impulses to pass along a SENSORY neurone into the spinal cord.

4 Electrical impulses are transmitted via a MOTOR neurone ...

1 A RECEPTOR is stimulated by the drawing pin (stimulus) ...

5 ... to the MUSCLES (effectors) causing them to CONTRACT in RESPONSE to the sharp drawing pin.

Types Of Receptor

- **LIGHT** RECEPTORS IN THE EYES.
- **SOUND** RECEPTORS IN THE EARS.
- **CHANGES OF POSITION** RECEPTORS IN THE EARS (for balance).
- **TASTE** RECEPTORS ON THE TONGUE.
- **SMELL** RECEPTORS IN THE NOSE.
- **TOUCH, PRESSURE AND TEMPERATURE** RECEPTORS IN THE SKIN.

The pathway for receiving information and then acting upon it is:

| STIMULUS | ⟹ | RECEPTOR | ⟹ | COORDINATOR (ANALYSER) | ⟹ | EFFECTOR | ⟹ | RESPONSE |

The coordinator is the central nervous system, to which impulses are transmitted via the spinal nerves.

Examples Of Responses To Stimuli

STIMULUS - change in the environment	RECEPTORS - detect stimuli	SENSORY NEURONE	CENTRAL NERVOUS SYSTEM	MOTOR NEURONE	EFFECTORS - muscles or glands	RESPONSE - action taken
BRIGHT LIGHT	Light sensitive receptors in the eye				Muscles in the eyelids	Eyelids close
LOUD MUSIC	Sound sensitive receptors in the ear				Muscles in arms and fingers	Turn music down
LOSING BALANCE	Receptors in the ear detect changes in position				Muscles in arms and legs	Move to regain balance
SMELL OF FOOD	Chemical sensitive receptors in nose				Salivary glands	Begin to salivate
SOUR TASTE	Chemical receptors on the tongue				Muscles in face	Cheeks sucked in
HOT PAN	Temperature receptors in the skin				Muscles in arms	Hand pulled away
SIT ON A DRAWING PIN	Pain receptors in the skin				Muscles in legs, tear glands	Jump up, eyes water
HAND BEING SQUEEZED HARD	Pressure receptors in the skin				Muscles in arms	Hand pulled away

The EFFECTORS are either MUSCLES or GLANDS.

These responses can be either ...

... CONSCIOUS RESPONSES, or ...

... REFLEX RESPONSES (see next page).

Conscious Action

After receiving a stimulus the body can make a considered response, ie. it acts consciously in making its response

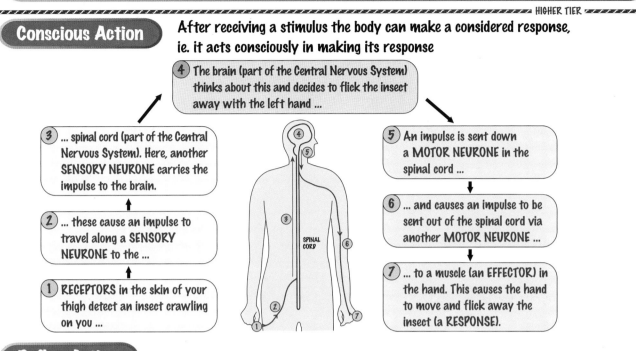

4 The brain (part of the Central Nervous System) thinks about this and decides to flick the insect away with the left hand ...

3 ... spinal cord (part of the Central Nervous System). Here, another SENSORY NEURONE carries the impulse to the brain.

2 ... these cause an impulse to travel along a SENSORY NEURONE to the ...

1 RECEPTORS in the skin of your thigh detect an insect crawling on you ...

5 An impulse is sent down a MOTOR NEURONE in the spinal cord ...

6 ... and causes an impulse to be sent out of the spinal cord via another MOTOR NEURONE ...

7 ... to a muscle (an EFFECTOR) in the hand. This causes the hand to move and flick away the insect (a RESPONSE).

Reflex Action

Sometimes 'Conscious Action' would be too slow to prevent harm to the body eg. putting your hand on a hot plate! 'Reflex Action' speeds up the response time by missing out the brain (steps **3** ⇨ **5** in the diagram above) completely. The spinal cord acts as the coordinator and passes impulses directly from a sensory neurone to a motor neurone via a RELAY NEURONE which 'short-circuits' the brain.

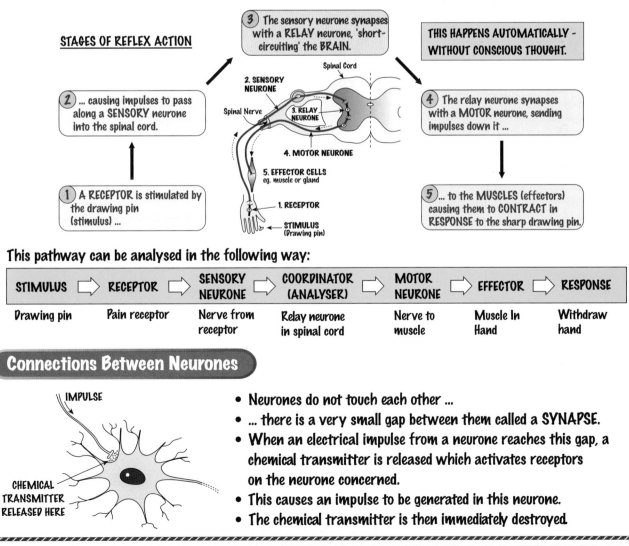

STAGES OF REFLEX ACTION

3 The sensory neurone synapses with a RELAY neurone, 'short-circuiting' the BRAIN.

THIS HAPPENS AUTOMATICALLY - WITHOUT CONSCIOUS THOUGHT.

2 ... causing impulses to pass along a SENSORY neurone into the spinal cord.

4 The relay neurone synapses with a MOTOR neurone, sending impulses down it ...

1 A RECEPTOR is stimulated by the drawing pin (stimulus) ...

5 ... to the MUSCLES (effectors) causing them to CONTRACT in RESPONSE to the sharp drawing pin.

Spinal Cord
2. SENSORY NEURONE
Spinal Nerve
3. RELAY NEURONE
4. MOTOR NEURONE
5. EFFECTOR CELLS eg. muscle or gland
1. RECEPTOR
STIMULUS (Drawing pin)

This pathway can be analysed in the following way:

STIMULUS	RECEPTOR	SENSORY NEURONE	COORDINATOR (ANALYSER)	MOTOR NEURONE	EFFECTOR	RESPONSE
Drawing pin	Pain receptor	Nerve from receptor	Relay neurone in spinal cord	Nerve to muscle	Muscle In Hand	Withdraw hand

Connections Between Neurones

IMPULSE

CHEMICAL TRANSMITTER RELEASED HERE

- Neurones do not touch each other ...
- ... there is a very small gap between them called a SYNAPSE.
- When an electrical impulse from a neurone reaches this gap, a chemical transmitter is released which activates receptors on the neurone concerned.
- This causes an impulse to be generated in this neurone.
- The chemical transmitter is then immediately destroyed.

The Structure Of The Eye

The eye is quite a complicated sense organ which focuses light onto light-sensitive receptor cells in the retina. These are then stimulated and cause nerve impulses to pass along sensory neurones to the brain.

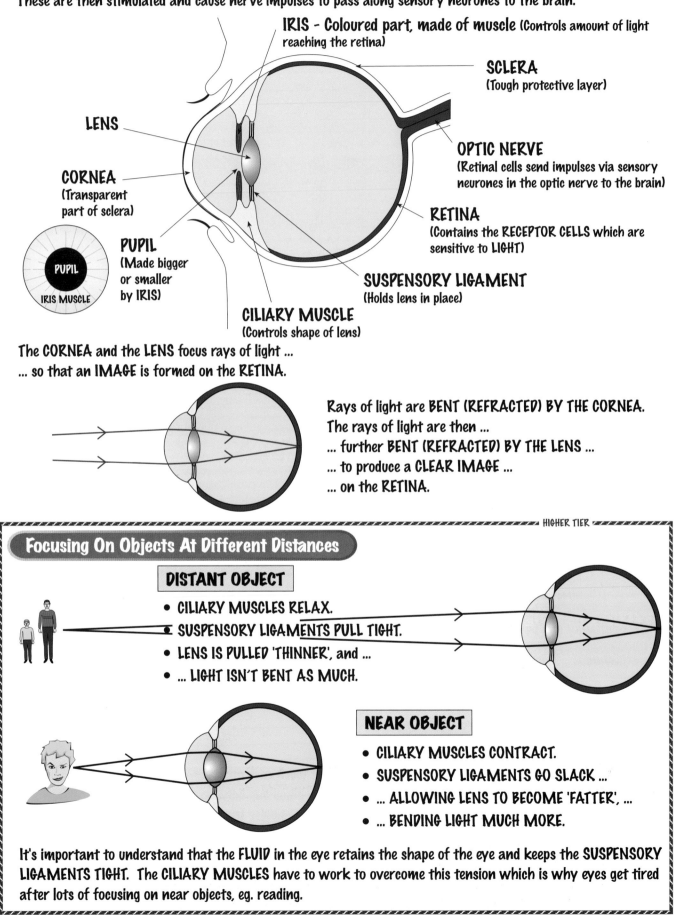

IRIS - Coloured part, made of muscle (Controls amount of light reaching the retina)

SCLERA (Tough protective layer)

LENS

OPTIC NERVE (Retinal cells send impulses via sensory neurones in the optic nerve to the brain)

CORNEA (Transparent part of sclera)

PUPIL

IRIS MUSCLE

RETINA (Contains the RECEPTOR CELLS which are sensitive to LIGHT)

PUPIL (Made bigger or smaller by IRIS)

SUSPENSORY LIGAMENT (Holds lens in place)

CILIARY MUSCLE (Controls shape of lens)

The CORNEA and the LENS focus rays of light ...
... so that an IMAGE is formed on the RETINA.

Rays of light are BENT (REFRACTED) BY THE CORNEA. The rays of light are then ...
... further BENT (REFRACTED) BY THE LENS ...
... to produce a CLEAR IMAGE ...
... on the RETINA.

━ HIGHER TIER ━

Focusing On Objects At Different Distances

DISTANT OBJECT
- CILIARY MUSCLES RELAX.
- SUSPENSORY LIGAMENTS PULL TIGHT.
- LENS IS PULLED 'THINNER', and ...
- ... LIGHT ISN'T BENT AS MUCH.

NEAR OBJECT
- CILIARY MUSCLES CONTRACT.
- SUSPENSORY LIGAMENTS GO SLACK ...
- ... ALLOWING LENS TO BECOME 'FATTER', ...
- ... BENDING LIGHT MUCH MORE.

It's important to understand that the FLUID in the eye retains the shape of the eye and keeps the SUSPENSORY LIGAMENTS TIGHT. The CILIARY MUSCLES have to work to overcome this tension which is why eyes get tired after lots of focusing on near objects, eg. reading.

Humans need to remove waste products from their body to keep their INTERNAL ENVIRONMENT relatively CONSTANT. Humans need to be at just the right temperature and have just the right amount of water and sugar in the bloodstream.

Waste Products Which Have To Be Removed

CARBON DIOXIDE	• Produced by RESPIRATION. Removed via the LUNGS when we breathe out.
UREA	• Produced by LIVER breaking down excess amino acids. • Removed by KIDNEYS, and transferred to the bladder before being released.

Internal Conditions Which Have To Be Controlled

WATER CONTENT	Water lost by:-	• breathing via lungs • sweating • excess via kidneys in urine
	Water gained by:-	• drinking
ION CONTENT (sodium, potassium etc.)	Ions are lost by:-	• sweating • excess via kidneys in urine
	Ions are gained by:-	• eating • drinking
TEMPERATURE (Ideally at 37°C) - because this is the temperature at which ENZYMES work best!	Temperature increased by:-	• shivering • 'shutting down' skin capillaries
	Temperature decreased by:-	• sweating • 'opening up' skin capillaries
BLOOD GLUCOSE	Blood glucose increased by:-	• hormone GLUCAGON (from the PANCREAS)
	Blood glucose decreased by:-	• hormone INSULIN (from the PANCREAS)

Hormones

Many processes within the body (including control of some of the above internal conditions) are coordinated by HORMONES. These are ...
• CHEMICAL 'MESSENGERS', secreted by GLANDS ...
• ... which are transported to their TARGET ORGANS by the BLOODSTREAM.

EXAMPLE-THE CONTROL OF BLOOD SUGAR LEVEL BY HORMONES PRODUCED IN THE PANCREAS

After a meal, the blood level of glucose rises as a result of carbohydrate digestion. The liver then starts to store this glucose and releases it only when the blood sugar level starts to fall.

Diabetes

This is a disease in which a person's blood glucose concentration may rise to a fatally high level because the pancreas does not produce enough insulin. This means that the liver doesn't convert glucose in the blood into insoluble glycogen for storage. Diabetes may be treated by careful attention to diet or by injecting insulin into the blood at appropriate times.

Control Of Blood Glucose Concentration

Blood glucose concentration is monitored and controlled by the PANCREAS which secretes two hormones, INSULIN and GLUCAGON, which act on the liver in the following ways ...

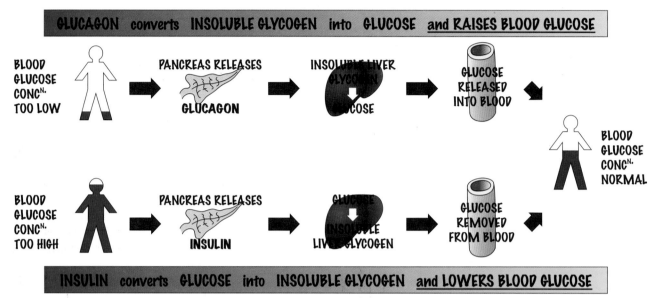

GLUCAGON converts INSOLUBLE GLYCOGEN into GLUCOSE and RAISES BLOOD GLUCOSE

BLOOD GLUCOSE CONCⁿ⁻ TOO LOW → PANCREAS RELEASES GLUCAGON → INSOLUBLE LIVER GLYCOGEN → GLUCOSE → GLUCOSE RELEASED INTO BLOOD → BLOOD GLUCOSE CONCⁿ⁻ NORMAL

BLOOD GLUCOSE CONCⁿ⁻ TOO HIGH → PANCREAS RELEASES INSULIN → GLUCOSE → INSOLUBLE LIVER GLYCOGEN → GLUCOSE REMOVED FROM BLOOD

INSULIN converts GLUCOSE into INSOLUBLE GLYCOGEN and LOWERS BLOOD GLUCOSE

The PANCREAS CONTINUALLY MONITORS the body's blood sugar levels and ADJUSTS THE AMOUNT of INSULIN and GLUCAGON released to keep the body's blood sugar levels AS CLOSE TO NORMAL as possible. The liver acts as a reservoir by storing blood glucose as insoluble glycogen when the blood glucose level is too high, and releasing it back into the blood as glucose when the level falls. This maintains the blood glucose level between fairly narrow boundaries.

Control Of Body Temperature

This is controlled by the NERVOUS SYSTEM.
- The CORE TEMPERATURE of the body should be kept at around 37°C (best for enzymes!).
- MONITORING AND CONTROL is done by the THERMOREGULATORY CENTRE in the BRAIN ...
  ... which has receptors which are sensitive to the temperature of the blood flowing through it.
- There are also temperature receptors in the skin which provide information about skin temperature.

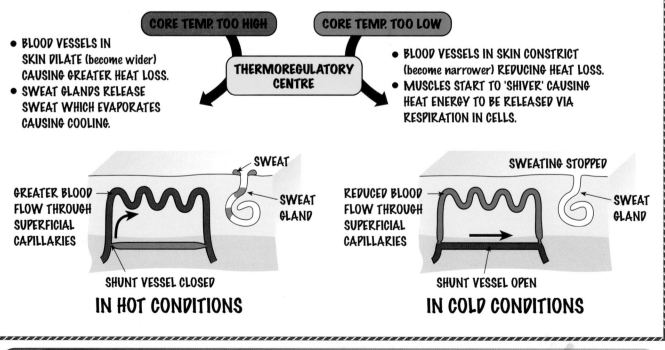

CORE TEMP. TOO HIGH — THERMOREGULATORY CENTRE — CORE TEMP. TOO LOW

- BLOOD VESSELS IN SKIN DILATE (become wider) CAUSING GREATER HEAT LOSS.
- SWEAT GLANDS RELEASE SWEAT WHICH EVAPORATES CAUSING COOLING.

- BLOOD VESSELS IN SKIN CONSTRICT (become narrower) REDUCING HEAT LOSS.
- MUSCLES START TO 'SHIVER' CAUSING HEAT ENERGY TO BE RELEASED VIA RESPIRATION IN CELLS.

GREATER BLOOD FLOW THROUGH SUPERFICIAL CAPILLARIES — SWEAT — SWEAT GLAND

SHUNT VESSEL CLOSED

IN HOT CONDITIONS

SWEATING STOPPED

REDUCED BLOOD FLOW THROUGH SUPERFICIAL CAPILLARIES — SWEAT GLAND

SHUNT VESSEL OPEN

IN COLD CONDITIONS

Control Of Ion Content And Excretion Of Urea

You don't need to understand the structure of the kidney but you do need to know how it works.
- Firstly, it is made up of two important tissues, BLOOD VESSELS and TUBULES.
- BLOOD VESSELS take the blood through the kidney where unwanted substances ...
- ... end up in millions of tiny TUBULES which eventually join together to form one tube ...
- ... the URETER which leaves the kidney and ends up at the BLADDER.

THE KIDNEY REGULATES THE AMOUNT OF WATER AND IONS IN THE BLOOD AND REMOVES <u>ALL</u> UREA.

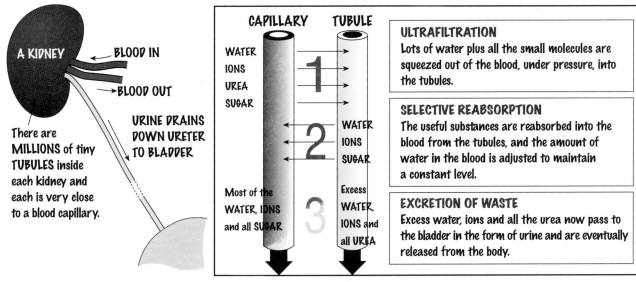

A KIDNEY — BLOOD IN — BLOOD OUT

URINE DRAINS DOWN URETER TO BLADDER

There are MILLIONS of tiny TUBULES inside each kidney and each is very close to a blood capillary.

CAPILLARY   TUBULE

WATER
IONS
UREA
SUGAR

WATER
IONS
SUGAR

Most of the WATER, IONS and all SUGAR

Excess WATER, IONS and all UREA

ULTRAFILTRATION
Lots of water plus all the small molecules are squeezed out of the blood, under pressure, into the tubules.

SELECTIVE REABSORPTION
The useful substances are reabsorbed into the blood from the tubules, and the amount of water in the blood is adjusted to maintain a constant level.

EXCRETION OF WASTE
Excess water, ions and all the urea now pass to the bladder in the form of urine and are eventually released from the body.

So, ... in principle there are THREE STAGES to learn ...

1. ... nearly everything is SQUEEZED OUT of the blood into the TUBULES ...
2. ... the substances we want to keep are REABSORBED back into the blood ...
3. ... unwanted substances are RELEASED as URINE.

Control Of Water Content – Effect Of A.D.H. On The Kidney

The amount of water reabsorbed by the kidneys in Stage 2 above is controlled by the hormone A.D.H. which is produced by the PITUITARY GLAND in the brain. A.D.H. directly affects the permeability (to water) of the kidney tubules.

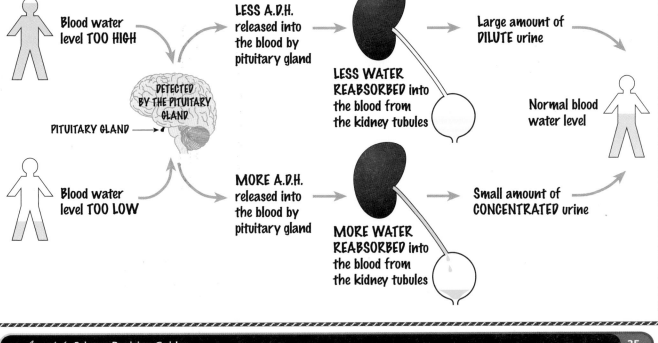

Blood water level TOO HIGH

LESS A.D.H. released into the blood by pituitary gland

LESS WATER REABSORBED into the blood from the kidney tubules

Large amount of DILUTE urine

Normal blood water level

DETECTED BY THE PITUITARY GLAND

PITUITARY GLAND →

Blood water level TOO LOW

MORE A.D.H. released into the blood by pituitary gland

MORE WATER REABSORBED into the blood from the kidney tubules

Small amount of CONCENTRATED urine

Fertility in women can be artificially controlled by giving ...
- ... Hormones that <u>stimulate</u> the release of eggs from the ovaries (FERTILITY DRUGS)
- ... Hormones that <u>prevent</u> the release of eggs from the ovaries (ORAL CONTRACEPTIVE PILLS)

- However, a woman produces hormones naturally that cause the release of an egg from her ovaries, ...
- ... and also cause the changes in the thickness of the lining of her womb.
- These hormones are produced by the PITUITARY GLAND and the OVARIES.

HIGHER TIER

Natural Control Of Fertility ... F.S.H., Oestrogen And L.H.

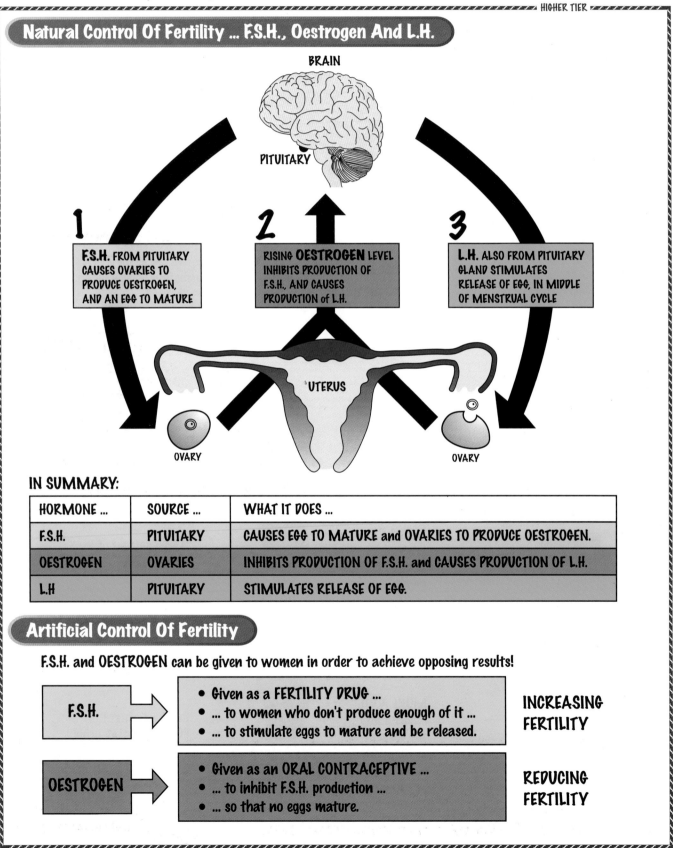

BRAIN

PITUITARY

1 F.S.H. FROM PITUITARY CAUSES OVARIES TO PRODUCE OESTROGEN, AND AN EGG TO MATURE

2 RISING OESTROGEN LEVEL INHIBITS PRODUCTION OF F.S.H., AND CAUSES PRODUCTION OF L.H.

3 L.H. ALSO FROM PITUITARY GLAND STIMULATES RELEASE OF EGG, IN MIDDLE OF MENSTRUAL CYCLE

UTERUS

OVARY   OVARY

IN SUMMARY:

HORMONE ...	SOURCE ...	WHAT IT DOES ...
F.S.H.	PITUITARY	CAUSES EGG TO MATURE and OVARIES TO PRODUCE OESTROGEN.
OESTROGEN	OVARIES	INHIBITS PRODUCTION OF F.S.H. and CAUSES PRODUCTION OF L.H.
L.H	PITUITARY	STIMULATES RELEASE OF EGG.

Artificial Control Of Fertility

F.S.H. and OESTROGEN can be given to women in order to achieve opposing results!

F.S.H. ➡
- Given as a FERTILITY DRUG ...
- ... to women who don't produce enough of it ...
- ... to stimulate eggs to mature and be released.

INCREASING FERTILITY

OESTROGEN ➡
- Given as an ORAL CONTRACEPTIVE ...
- ... to inhibit F.S.H. production ...
- ... so that no eggs mature.

REDUCING FERTILITY

Bacteria And Viruses

These are the two main types of microorganism which may affect health.

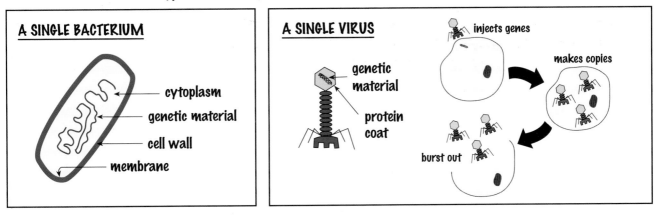

A SINGLE BACTERIUM
- cytoplasm
- genetic material
- cell wall
- membrane

A SINGLE VIRUS
- genetic material
- protein coat

injects genes
makes copies
burst out

A Comparison Between Bacteria And Viruses

BACTERIA	VIRUSES
Consist of CYTOPLASM and a MEMBRANE surrounded by a CELL WALL.	Have a simple PROTEIN COAT. No membrane or cell wall.
The genetic material is NOT contained within a NUCLEUS.	The genetic material is NOT contained within a NUCLEUS.
Very small.	Even smaller.
Reproduce very quickly.	Reproduce very quickly - BUT ONLY INSIDE LIVING CELLS, WHICH ARE THEN DAMAGED. (see above)
Can produce TOXINS (poisons) which make us feel ill.	Can produce TOXINS (poisons) which make us feel ill.
Responsible for diseases such as TETANUS, CHOLERA, TUBERCULOSIS.	Responsible for diseases such as COLDS, FLU, MEASLES, POLIO.

- Microorganisms can ENTER THE BODY through NATURAL OPENINGS (eg. the nose or mouth) ...
  ... and through BREAKS IN THE SKIN (cuts, bites).
- If LARGE NUMBERS OF MICROORGANISMS enter the body due to UNHYGIENIC CONDITIONS ...
  ... or contact with INFECTED PEOPLE ...
  ... the MICROORGANISMS can REPRODUCE RAPIDLY and make the person unwell.

Our Defence Against Microorganisms

1. The blood produces CLOTS that seal cuts.

2. The BREATHING ORGANS produce a STICKY, LIQUID MUCUS, which covers the lining of these organs and traps microorganisms.

3. The SKIN acts as a barrier to invading microorganisms.

4. The white cells
   - When a microorganism invades the body and starts to multiply ...
   - ... the body's WHITE CELLS multiply in response. (see next page).

A white cell ingesting (eating) microorganisms.

The **WHITE BLOOD CELLS** form part of the body's **IMMUNE SYSTEM**.
White blood cells work by ...

1. INGESTING MICROORGANISMS.
2. PRODUCING ANTITOXINS to NEUTRALISE TOXINS produced by the microorganisms.
3. PRODUCING ANTIBODIES to DESTROY PARTICULAR MICROORGANISMS.

Ingesting Microorganisms

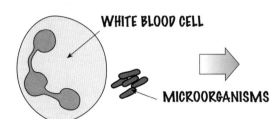

Microorganisms invade the body ...

... the white blood cell starts to surround the microorganisms.

The microorganisms are INGESTED by the white blood cell.

Producing Antitoxins

White blood cells produce **ANTITOXINS** which **NEUTRALISE HARMFUL TOXINS** (poisons) produced by microorganisms.

Producing Antibodies

- **WHITE BLOOD CELLS** recognise the microorganisms as **ANTIGENS** (foreign bodies) ...
  ... and produce **ANTIBODIES** to destroy the **ANTIGENS**. (Often by making them clump together!).
- The reason we feel **ILL** is because it takes **TIME** for the **WHITE BLOOD CELLS** to produce **ANTIBODIES** to the microorganisms.
- The **PRODUCTION OF ANTIBODIES** is much faster if a person has already had the infectious disease. The **WHITE BLOOD CELLS** seem to 'remember' the antigen and in the future can produce **ANTIBODIES** more rapidly providing the person with a **NATURAL IMMUNITY**.

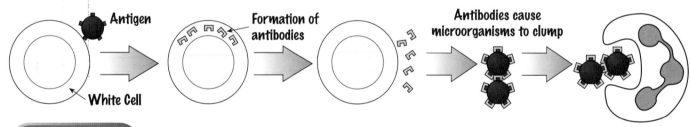

Vaccination

A person can acquire immunity to a particular disease by being vaccinated ...

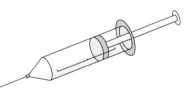

STEP 1: A WEAKENED or DEAD ANTIGEN is injected into a person.
STEP 2: The body PRODUCES ANTIBODIES to fight the antigen.
STEP 3: The body now has an acquired immunity to this particular antigen since the white blood cells are now sensitised to it and will therefore respond to any future infection by producing antibodies very quickly.

DRUGS are chemical substances which ALTER THE WAY THE BODY WORKS.

Some drugs can be obtained from LIVING THINGS, others are SYNTHETIC (MAN-MADE).

Some drugs are called MEDICINES and these are taken to CURE ILLNESSES or EASE THE SYMPTOMS produced during an illness. Examples include PAIN-KILLERS and ANTIBIOTICS (which destroy bacteria and some other microorganisms).

Alcohol, Tobacco And Solvents

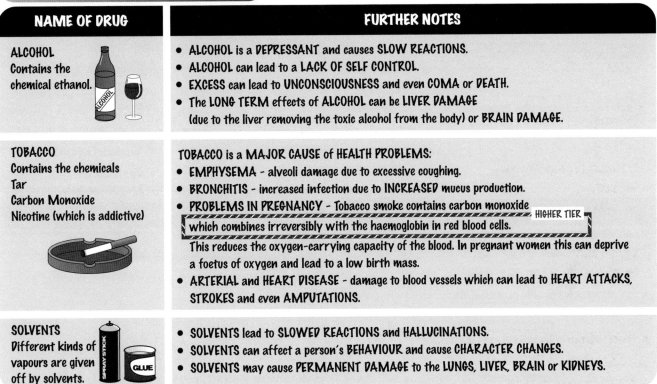

NAME OF DRUG	FURTHER NOTES
ALCOHOL Contains the chemical ethanol.	• ALCOHOL is a DEPRESSANT and causes SLOW REACTIONS. • ALCOHOL can lead to a LACK OF SELF CONTROL. • EXCESS can lead to UNCONSCIOUSNESS and even COMA or DEATH. • The LONG TERM effects of ALCOHOL can be LIVER DAMAGE (due to the liver removing the toxic alcohol from the body) or BRAIN DAMAGE.
TOBACCO Contains the chemicals Tar Carbon Monoxide Nicotine (which is addictive)	TOBACCO is a MAJOR CAUSE of HEALTH PROBLEMS: • EMPHYSEMA - alveoli damage due to excessive coughing. • BRONCHITIS - increased infection due to INCREASED mucus production. • PROBLEMS IN PREGNANCY - Tobacco smoke contains carbon monoxide HIGHER TIER which combines irreversibly with the haemoglobin in red blood cells. This reduces the oxygen-carrying capacity of the blood. In pregnant women this can deprive a foetus of oxygen and lead to a low birth mass. • ARTERIAL and HEART DISEASE - damage to blood vessels which can lead to HEART ATTACKS, STROKES and even AMPUTATIONS.
SOLVENTS Different kinds of vapours are given off by solvents.	• SOLVENTS lead to SLOWED REACTIONS and HALLUCINATIONS. • SOLVENTS can affect a person's BEHAVIOUR and cause CHARACTER CHANGES. • SOLVENTS may cause PERMANENT DAMAGE to the LUNGS, LIVER, BRAIN or KIDNEYS.

People may become dependent or ADDICTED to certain drugs and may therefore suffer WITHDRAWAL SYMPTOMS without them. These may be psychological or physical (such as sweating, shaking, feeling sick or vomiting.)

The Link Between Lung Cancer And Smoking

The marked increase in deaths from lung cancer during the 1940's and 1950's prompted scientists to investigate the cause by monitoring a group of smokers and a group of non-smokers over a long period of time. This study showed that smokers were more likely to get lung cancer than non-smokers, and that the more a person smoked, the greater their chances of getting lung cancer.

The non-smokers in this study are called the control group and as far as possible would be in the same age range and same occupational groups as the smokers. In other words, ideally you want the control group to differ from the smoking group only because they don't smoke.

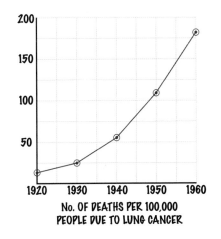

No. OF DEATHS PER 100,000 PEOPLE DUE TO LUNG CANCER

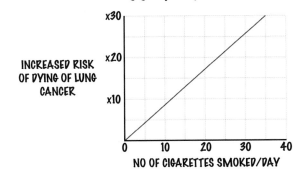

INCREASED RISK OF DYING OF LUNG CANCER

NO OF CIGARETTES SMOKED/DAY

Being a smoker doesn't mean that you will definitely get lung cancer any more than being a non-smoker means that you definitely won't get it. However, your chances are increased, and the more you smoke the greater your chances are increased.

THE NERVOUS SYSTEM I

- The nervous system consists of the BRAIN, SPINAL CORD, PAIRED SPINAL NERVES and the RECEPTORS.
- Receptors may be sensitive to LIGHT, SOUND, POSITION, SMELL, TASTE, TEMPERATURE, PAIN and PRESSURE.

TYPES OF NEURONE

MOTOR NEURONE

SENSORY NEURONE

REFLEX ACTION

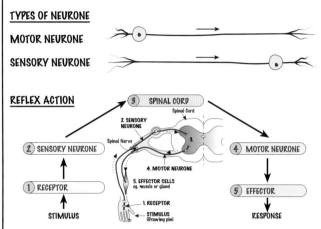

THE NERVOUS SYSTEM II

In REFLEX ACTION, stage three is actually performed by a RELAY NEURONE within the spinal cord. This pathway may be analysed as ...

STIMULUS → RECEPTOR → COORDINATOR (ANALYSER) → EFFECTOR → RESPONSE

NEURONES are well-adapted to their function because they are LONG and BRANCHED

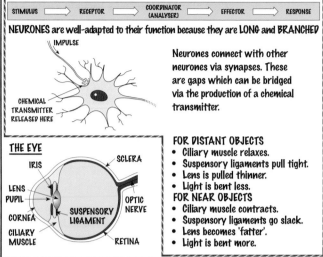

Neurones connect with other neurones via synapses. These are gaps which can be bridged via the production of a chemical transmitter.

THE EYE

FOR DISTANT OBJECTS
- Ciliary muscle relaxes.
- Suspensory ligaments pull tight.
- Lens is pulled thinner.
- Light is bent less.

FOR NEAR OBJECTS
- Ciliary muscle contracts.
- Suspensory ligaments go slack.
- Lens becomes 'fatter'.
- Light is bent more.

CONTROLLING INTERNAL ENVIRONMENT I

CO_2 and urea must be removed, and water content, ion content, temperature and blood glucose must be controlled. Much of this is hormonal. Hormones are ...
- CHEMICAL SUBSTANCES secreted by GLANDS ...
- ... which are transported to their TARGET ORGANS by the BLOODSTREAM.

WASTE PRODUCTS WHICH HAVE TO BE REMOVED

| CARBON DIOXIDE | • Produced by RESPIRATION. Removed via the LUNGS when we breathe out. |
| UREA | • Produced by LIVER breaking down excess amino acids. • Removed by KIDNEYS, and transferred to the bladder before being released. |

INTERNAL CONDITIONS WHICH HAVE TO BE CONTROLLED

WATER CONTENT	Water lost by:-	• breathing via lungs • sweating • excess via kidneys in urine
	Water gained by:-	• drinking
ION CONTENT (Sodium, Potassium etc.)	Ions are lost by:-	• sweating • excess via kidneys in urine
	Ions are gained by:-	• eating • drinking
TEMPERATURE (Ideally at 37°C) - because this is the temperature at which ENZYMES work best!	Temperature increased by:-	• shivering • 'shutting down' skin capillaries
	Temperature decreased by:-	• sweating • 'opening up' skin capillaries
BLOOD GLUCOSE	Blood glucose increased by:-	• hormone GLUCAGON (from the PANCREAS)
	Blood glucose decreased by:-	• hormone INSULIN (from the PANCREAS)

DIABETES Pancreas doesn't secrete enough INSULIN. Can be treated by DIET or INJECTING INSULIN.

CONTROLLING INTERNAL ENVIRONMENT II

ION, UREA + WATER CONTENT

Between the vessels and the tubules, the following three processes occur ...

① ULTRA FILTRATION ② SELECTIVE REABSORPTION ③ EXCRETION OF WASTE

H_2O TOO HIGH → PITUITARY DETECTS → LESS ADH → LESS REABSORPTION FROM TUBULES → MORE DILUTE URINE ↘ NORMAL BLOOD WATER LEVEL

H_2O TOO LOW → PITUITARY DETECTS → MORE ADH → MORE REABSORPTION FROM TUBULES → LITTLE CONCENTRATED URINE ↗

BLOOD GLUCOSE CONCENTRATION

GLUCOSE TOO LOW → PANCREAS RELEASES GLUCAGON → LIVER GLYCOGEN ↓ GLUCOSE → GLUCOSE INTO BLOOD ↘ NORMAL GLUCOSE LEVEL

GLUCOSE TOO HIGH → PANCREAS RELEASES INSULIN → GLUCOSE ↓ LIVER GLYCOGEN → GLUCOSE OUT OF BLOOD ↗

BODY TEMPERATURE Thermoregulatory centre

SKIN CAPILLARY DILATION + SWEATING IF TEMPERATURE TOO HIGH v SKIN CAPILLARY CONSTRICTION + SHIVERING IF TEMPERATURE TOO LOW

FERTILITY AND DRUGS

Release of an egg and thickening of the womb lining are controlled by hormones from the PITUITARY GLAND and the OVARIES.

FERTILITY DRUGS stimulate egg release.

CONTRACEPTIVE PILLS prevent egg release.

HORMONE ...	SOURCE ...	WHAT IT DOES ...
F.S.H.	PITUITARY	CAUSES EGG TO MATURE and OVARIES TO PRODUCE OESTROGEN.
OESTROGEN	OVARIES	INHIBITS PRODUCTION OF F.S.H. and CAUSES PRODUCTION OF L.H.
L.H.	PITUITARY	STIMULATES RELEASE OF EGG.

ARTIFICIAL CONTROL OF FERTILITY

| F.S.H. | • Given as a FERTILITY DRUG ... • ... to women who don't produce enough of it ... • ... to stimulate eggs to mature and be released. | INCREASING FERTILITY |
| OESTROGEN | • Given as an ORAL CONTRACEPTIVE ... • ... to inhibit F.S.H. production ... • ... so that no eggs mature. | REDUCING FERTILITY |

DRUGS: (Alcohol) affects the nervous system and can cause damage to the liver and brain.
(Solvents) affect behaviour and can damage the lungs, liver and brain.
(Tobacco) contains addictive nicotine and can cause lung cancer, bronchitis, emphysema and heart disease. Can lead to 'low birth' weights in infants.

DISEASE AND THE WHITE CELLS

Clotting, mucus, skin and white cells are our basic defence against microorganisms. BACTERIUM VIRUS

BACTERIA	VIRUSES
Consist of CYTOPLASM and a MEMBRANE surrounded by a CELL WALL.	Have a simple PROTEIN COAT. No membrane or cell wall.
The genetic material is NOT contained within a NUCLEUS.	The genetic material is NOT contained within a NUCLEUS.
Very small.	Even smaller.
Reproduce very quickly.	Reproduce very quickly - BUT ONLY INSIDE LIVING CELLS, WHICH ARE THEN DAMAGED.
Can produce TOXINS (poisons) which make us feel ill.	Can produce TOXINS (poisons) which make us feel ill.
Responsible for diseases such as TETANUS, CHOLERA, TUBERCULOSIS.	Responsible for diseases such as COLDS, FLU, MEASLES, POLIO.

WHITE CELLS can ...
INGEST microorganisms, produce ANTITOXINS, produce ANTIBODIES!

ANTIBODY PRODUCTION INGESTION

After being exposed to certain microorganisms, our bodies can produce antibodies quicker next time. We have developed NATURAL IMMUNITY.
ACQUIRED IMMUNITY can be developed by being injected with a dead or weakened version of the microorganism.

SUMMARY QUESTIONS

1. a) Receptors positioned all over the body can detect changes in the environment.
   The human ear has two different types of receptor. What do each of them detect?
   b) Describe the function of two different types of receptor in the skin.

2. a) Fill in the missing words in the following sequence.

   STIMULUS → _____ → SENSORY → _____ → MOTOR → _____ → RESPONSE
                              NEURONE   NEURONE

   b) Label the diagram opposite which shows a section of the spinal cord.
   c) Explain how these three structures work together in a reflex action.
   d) What is a synapse?
   e) What is the purpose of reflex action?

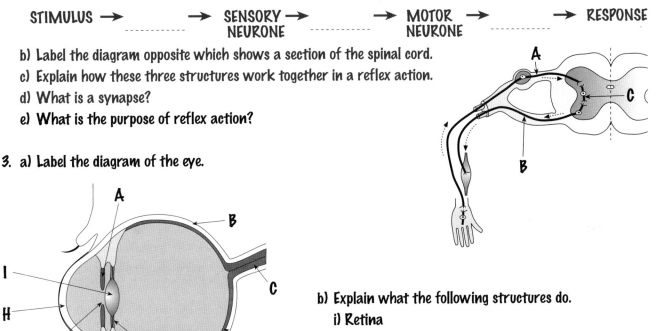

3. a) Label the diagram of the eye.

   b) Explain what the following structures do.
      i) Retina
      ii) Ciliary muscles
      iii) Iris

   c) Explain what must happen to the ciliary muscles, suspensory ligaments and lens when the eye focuses on a near object.
   d) Explain what must happen to the ciliary muscles, suspensory ligaments and lens when the eye focuses on a far away object.

4. What is the function of:
   a) The sclera
   b) The cornea
   c) The suspensory ligaments
   d) The optic nerve

5. Give an example of an effector and explain what it can do.

6. Describe the reflex action which might take place if someone was stung by a nettle. Analyse each stage of the action in terms of stimulus, receptor, coordinator, effector and response.

7. a) The blood glucose and the ion content of the body are just two internal conditions which must be constantly monitored and controlled. Name two other internal conditions which must be controlled.

    b) Explain briefly how the body attempts to control them.

8. a) Name two waste products which must be removed from the body.

    b) Explain how the body removes them.

9. a) Explain how the pancreas and liver can reduce the amount of glucose in the blood.

    b) Explain how the pancreas and liver can increase the amount of glucose in the blood.

10. a) Describe the changes which may take place in the skin of a human who gets warm by doing vigorous exercise.

    b) Describe the changes which may take place in the skin of a human who gets too cold on a Winter's afternoon.

11. a) Name four substances which are filtered out of the blood under high pressure in the kidneys.

    b) Which one of these substances is completely reabsorbed into the blood?

    c) Describe what happens when the amount of water in the blood becomes too high.

    d) Describe what happens when the amount of water in the blood becomes too low.

12. a) Describe how hormones influence the natural control of fertility.

    b) Describe how hormones can be used artificially to increase fertility.

    c) Describe how hormones can be used artificially to reduce fertility.

13. a) List three differences between bacteria and viruses.

    b) List four defence mechanisms against microbes which the human body has.

    c) Explain what is meant by ...

       i) Antitoxins

       ii) Antibodies

       iii) Vaccination

       iv) Immunity

14. List three problems which can be caused by ...

    a) Solvents

    b) Tobacco

    c) Alcohol

Causes Of Variation

Differences between individuals of the same species is described as VARIATION.

Variation may be due to ...

- ... GENETIC CAUSES because of the different genes they have inherited, or ...
- ... ENVIRONMENTAL CAUSES because of the conditions in which they have developed.

However, usually **VARIATION IS DUE TO A COMBINATION OF GENETIC AND ENVIRONMENTAL CAUSES**

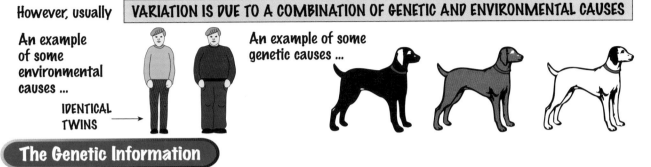

An example of some environmental causes ...

IDENTICAL TWINS

An example of some genetic causes ...

The Genetic Information

This information is carried by GENES which are found on CHROMOSOMES.

Different genes control the development of different characteristics.

Many genes have different forms called ALLELES which may produce different characteristics ie. genes for brown eyes and genes for blue eyes are ALLELES; in other words different forms of the same gene!

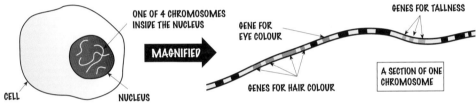

ONE OF 4 CHROMOSOMES INSIDE THE NUCLEUS

GENES FOR TALLNESS

GENE FOR EYE COLOUR

MAGNIFIED

A SECTION OF ONE CHROMOSOME

CELL

NUCLEUS

GENES FOR HAIR COLOUR

Chromosomes come in PAIRS, but different species have different numbers of pairs ...

eg. Humans have 23 pairs. The example above has just 2 pairs!

Mutations

New forms of genes can arise from changes (MUTATIONS) in existing genes.

Mutations occur naturally, but their frequency is increased by ...

- EXPOSURE TO ULTRA-VIOLET LIGHT
- EXPOSURE TO X-RAYS
- EXPOSURE TO RADIOACTIVE SUBSTANCES
- EXPOSURE TO CERTAIN CHEMICALS

Effect Of Reproduction On Variation

SEXUAL REPRODUCTION means LOADS OF VARIATION because ...

... genetic information from two parents is 'mixed together' ...

... when the male (sperm) and female (egg) gametes fuse!!

The sperm contains 23 chromosomes from the father while the egg contains 23 chromosomes from the mother.

The fusion of these two cells produces a ZYGOTE with 23 <u>pairs</u> of chromosomes (or 46 chromosomes).

All the body cells produced from this one cell will also contain 46 chromosomes.

23

23

46

(23 pairs actually!)

ASEXUAL REPRODUCTION means NO VARIATION AT ALL because ...

... only one individual is needed as the single parent for it to take place, so ...

... individuals who are genetically identical to the parent (CLONES) are produced.

Bacteria reproducing ASEXUALLY

Mitosis

This occurs for GROWTH and REPAIR (and also in asexual reproduction) and before each cell division a copy of each chromosome is made so that each body cell has exactly the same genetic information.

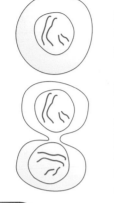

PARENTAL CELL WITH TWO PAIRS OF CHROMOSOMES.

EACH CHROMOSOME REPLICATES ITSELF.

EACH 'DAUGHTER' CELL HAS THE SAME NUMBER OF CHROMOSOMES AS THE PARENTAL CELL, AND CONTAINS THE SAME GENES AS THE PARENTAL CELL.

THE 'COPIES' ARE PULLED APART. CELL NOW DIVIDES FOR THE ONLY TIME.

Meiosis

This occurs in the testes and ovaries to produce the gametes (eggs and sperm) for SEXUAL REPRODUCTION.

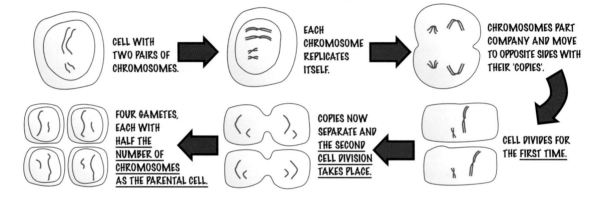

CELL WITH TWO PAIRS OF CHROMOSOMES.

EACH CHROMOSOME REPLICATES ITSELF.

CHROMOSOMES PART COMPANY AND MOVE TO OPPOSITE SIDES WITH THEIR 'COPIES'.

FOUR GAMETES, EACH WITH HALF THE NUMBER OF CHROMOSOMES AS THE PARENTAL CELL.

COPIES NOW SEPARATE AND THE SECOND CELL DIVISION TAKES PLACE.

CELL DIVIDES FOR THE FIRST TIME.

Fertilisation

When gametes join at fertilisation, a single body cell with NEW PAIRS OF CHROMOSOMES is formed. This then divides repeatedly by MITOSIS to form a new individual ...

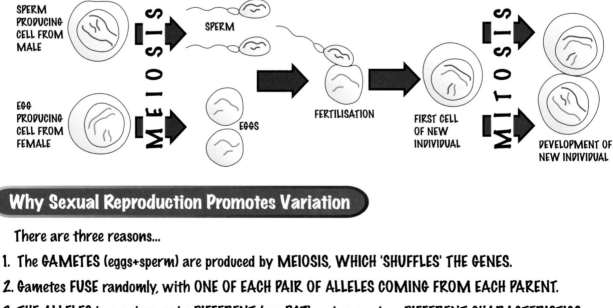

SPERM PRODUCING CELL FROM MALE

MEIOSIS

SPERM

EGG PRODUCING CELL FROM FEMALE

MEIOSIS

EGGS

FERTILISATION

FIRST CELL OF NEW INDIVIDUAL

MITOSIS

MITOSIS

DEVELOPMENT OF NEW INDIVIDUAL

Why Sexual Reproduction Promotes Variation

There are three reasons...

1. The GAMETES (eggs+sperm) are produced by MEIOSIS, WHICH 'SHUFFLES' THE GENES.

2. Gametes FUSE randomly, with ONE OF EACH PAIR OF ALLELES COMING FROM EACH PARENT.

3. THE ALLELES in a pair may be DIFFERENT (see P.47) and so produce DIFFERENT CHARACTERISTICS.

Genes, Chromosomes And DNA

- In normal human cells, there are only **23** pairs of chromosomes. They consist of long, coiled molecules of DNA.
- Genes are sections of DNA which code for a particular inherited characteristic eg. blue eyes.

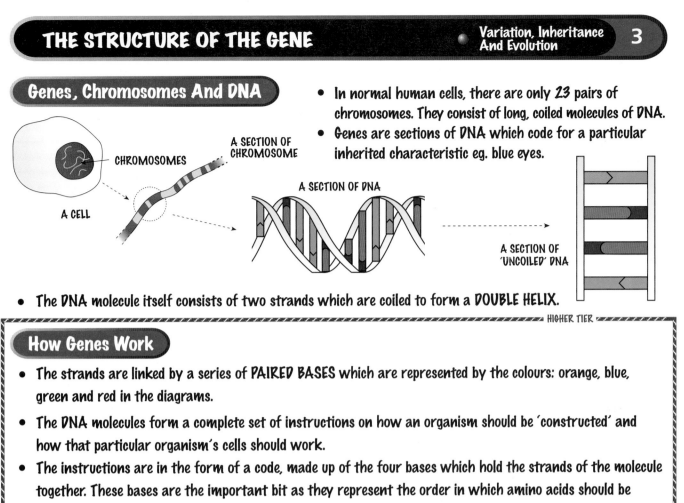

CHROMOSOMES

A CELL

A SECTION OF CHROMOSOME

A SECTION OF DNA

A SECTION OF 'UNCOILED' DNA

- The DNA molecule itself consists of two strands which are coiled to form a **DOUBLE HELIX**.

HIGHER TIER

How Genes Work

- The strands are linked by a series of **PAIRED BASES** which are represented by the colours: orange, blue, green and red in the diagrams.

- The DNA molecules form a complete set of instructions on how an organism should be 'constructed' and how that particular organism's cells should work.

- The instructions are in the form of a code, made up of the four bases which hold the strands of the molecule together. These bases are the important bit as they represent the order in which amino acids should be assembled to make proteins in living cells. Each group of three bases represents one amino acid in a protein chain.

- Since there are only about 20 amino acids, the code contained in the four bases is quite sufficient.

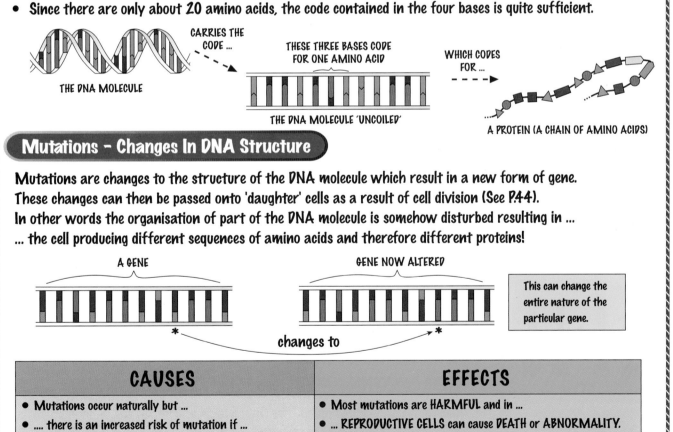

THE DNA MOLECULE

CARRIES THE CODE ...

THESE THREE BASES CODE FOR ONE AMINO ACID

THE DNA MOLECULE 'UNCOILED'

WHICH CODES FOR ...

A PROTEIN (A CHAIN OF AMINO ACIDS)

Mutations – Changes In DNA Structure

Mutations are changes to the structure of the DNA molecule which result in a new form of gene.
These changes can then be passed onto 'daughter' cells as a result of cell division (See P.44).
In other words the organisation of part of the DNA molecule is somehow disturbed resulting in ...
... the cell producing different sequences of amino acids and therefore different proteins!

A GENE

GENE NOW ALTERED

This can change the entire nature of the particular gene.

changes to

CAUSES	EFFECTS
• Mutations occur naturally but ...	• Most mutations are HARMFUL and in ...
• .... there is an increased risk of mutation if ...	• ... REPRODUCTIVE CELLS can cause DEATH or ABNORMALITY.
• ... individuals are exposed to MUTAGENIC AGENTS ...	• In BODY CELLS they may cause CANCER.
• ... eg. IONISING RADIATION (inc U-V LIGHT, X-RAYS) ...	• Some mutations are NEUTRAL, and in RARE CASES ...
• ... RADIOACTIVE SUBSTANCES and CERTAIN CHEMICALS.	• ... may INCREASE THE SURVIVAL CHANCES OF AN ORGANISM.
• THE GREATER THE DOSE, THE GREATER THE RISK.	• ... and its OFFSPRING WHO INHERIT THE GENE.

Inheritance Of Sex – The Sex Chromosomes

- Humans have 23 pairs of CHROMOSOMES, of which one pair are the SEX CHROMOSOMES.

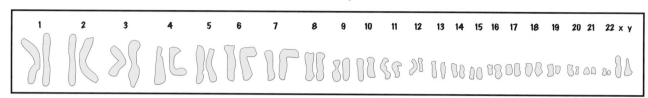

- In females these are IDENTICAL and are called the X chromosomes.
- In males ONE IS MUCH SHORTER THAN THE OTHER and they're called the X and Y chromosomes (Y being the shorter).

THE POSSIBLE PERMUTATIONS

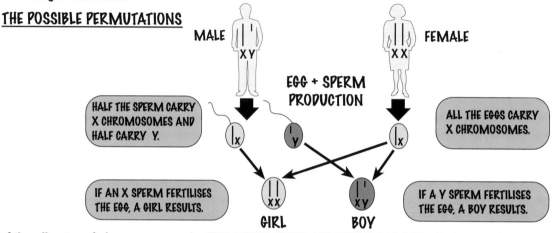

MALE XY   FEMALE XX

EGG + SPERM PRODUCTION

HALF THE SPERM CARRY X CHROMOSOMES AND HALF CARRY Y.

ALL THE EGGS CARRY X CHROMOSOMES.

IF AN X SPERM FERTILISES THE EGG, A GIRL RESULTS.

IF A Y SPERM FERTILISES THE EGG, A BOY RESULTS.

GIRL   BOY

- Like all pairs of chromosomes, the SEX CHROMOSOMES SEPARATE DURING EGG + SPERM PRODUCTION ...
- ... (ie. meiosis) resulting in just one in each sperm or egg.

Ultimately, therefore, the sex of an individual is decided by whether the ovum is fertilised by an X-carrying sperm or a Y-carrying sperm.

Gregor Mendel

- GREGOR MENDEL was born in Austria in 1822 ...
  ... his WORK on PEA PLANTS in 1865 marks the START OF MODERN GENETICS.
- He investigated the HEIGHT OF PEA PLANTS which are all either TALL or DWARF.

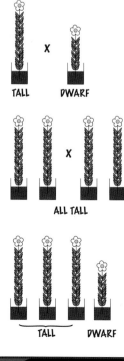

- Mendel started off by taking a plant which was pure-breeding for TALLNESS (ie. when bred with itself or other tall plants they only produced tall plants).
- He then took a plant which was pure breeding for DWARFNESS (ie. it only produced dwarf plants when bred with itself or other dwarf plants).
- He then cross-fertilised these two plants by taking pollen from each one.

- To Mendel's surprise ALL the plants produced from the cross were TALL. Mendel based his first law on this which said ...
- 'When pure-breeding plants with contrasting traits are crossed, all the offspring will resemble ONE of the parents'.
- Mendel then crossed several of these tall plants which he had produced.

- Again to his surprise he found that there was a 3:1 ratio of tall to dwarf plants. Mendel based his second law on this which said...
- 'For every trait, every individual must have two determiners'.
- We realise now of course that these 'determiners' are GENES but at the time nobody knew about these things. Consequently it was not until 1900 that people recognised the significance of his results.

There are several long words associated with genetics, but don't be put off. The more you use them, the more familiar they will become to you. Here they are ...

ALLELE This is an ALTERNATIVE FORM of a gene. So, for instance, if we were talking about genes for eye colour, we would say that there were two alleles for eye colour, brown and blue. Similarly the genes for being able/not able to roll your tongue are alleles.

DOMINANT This refers to an allele which controls the development of a characteristic when it is present on only one of the chromosomes in a pair.

RECESSIVE This refers to an allele which controls the development of a characteristic only if a dominant allele is not present.

FOR EXAMPLE It's perhaps a little easier to understand if we look at a diagram of a ...
... pair of chromosomes and specifically at genes which code for ...
... eye colour, tongue-rolling ability, and type of ear lobe.

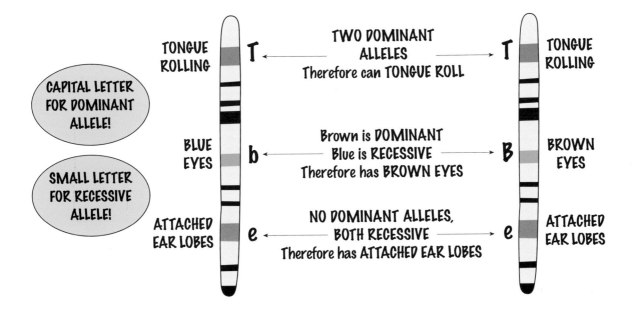

CAPITAL LETTER FOR DOMINANT ALLELE!

SMALL LETTER FOR RECESSIVE ALLELE!

TONGUE ROLLING — **T** — TWO DOMINANT ALLELES Therefore can TONGUE ROLL — **T** — TONGUE ROLLING

BLUE EYES — **b** — Brown is DOMINANT Blue is RECESSIVE Therefore has BROWN EYES — **B** — BROWN EYES

ATTACHED EAR LOBES — **e** — NO DOMINANT ALLELES, BOTH RECESSIVE Therefore has ATTACHED EAR LOBES — **e** — ATTACHED EAR LOBES

HIGHER TIER

- **DOMINANT ALLELES EXPRESS THEMSELVES IF PRESENT ONLY ONCE ...**
  ... so an individual can be HOMOZYGOUS DOMINANT (BB) or HETEROZYGOUS (Bb) for brown eyes.
- **RECESSIVE ALLELES EXPRESS THEMSELVES ONLY IF PRESENT TWICE ...**
  ... so an individual can only be HOMOZYGOUS RECESSIVE (bb) for blue eyes.

So the possible combinations are ...

	HOMOZYGOUS DOMINANT	HETEROZYGOUS	HOMOZYGOUS RECESSIVE
TONGUE ROLLING	TT (can roll)	Tt (can roll)	tt (can't roll)
EYE COLOUR	BB (brown)	Bb (brown)	bb (blue)
EAR LOBES	EE (free lobes)	Ee (free lobes)	ee (attached lobes)

HOMOZYGOUS If both chromosomes in a pair contain the same allele of a gene then the individual is homozygous for that gene or condition.

HETEROZYGOUS If the chromosomes in a pair contain different alleles of a gene then the individual is heterozygous for that gene or condition.

HIGHER TIER

Monohybrid Inheritance – An Explanation.

As we saw on previous pages, genes exist in pairs; one on each of a pair of chromosomes. We call these pairs of genes alleles when they code for alternatives of the same characteristic eg. eye colour. When a characteristic is determined by just one pair of alleles then simple genetic crosses can be performed to investigate the mechanism of inheritance. This type of inheritance is referred to as MONOHYBRID INHERITANCE.

Inheritance Of Eye Colour

In genetic diagrams we use CAPITAL LETTERS FOR DOMINANT ALLELES and LOWER CASE FOR RECESSIVE ALLELES. In eye colour therefore we use B for brown eye alleles and b for blue eye alleles ...

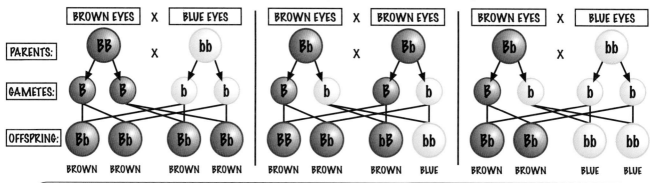

These are the typical examples you may be asked about in your exam. REMEMBER ...
to clearly identify the alleles of the parents ...
to place each of these alleles in a separate gamete ...
and then join each gamete with the two gametes from the OTHER PARENT!!

From the crosses above it can be seen that ...
... if one parent has 2 dominant genes then all the offspring will inherit that characteristic.
... if both parents have 1 recessive gene then this characteristic may appear in the offspring (a 1 in 4 chance).
... if one parent has a recessive gene and the other has 2, then there's a 50% chance of that characteristic appearing. But remember, these are only probabilities. In practice, all that matters is which egg is fertilised by which sperm!

More Advanced Genetics Problems

These usually involve 'wordy' descriptions which you have to translate into crosses.

EXAMPLE 1 Draw genetic diagrams to predict the probable outcome when two heterozygous brown eyed people mate. Brown eyes are dominant to blue eyes.

A The genetic diagram reveals a 3:1 ratio of brown eyes to blue eyes.

EXAMPLE 2 In mice, white fur is dominant. What type of offspring would you expect to be produced from a cross between a heterozygous individual and one with grey fur? Support your answer with a genetic diagram.

A There is a 1:1 ratio of heterozygous individuals to homozygous recessive individuals.

EXAMPLE 3 A homozygous long tailed cat is crossed with a homozygous short tailed cat and produces a litter of 9 long tailed kittens. Show the probable offspring which would be produced if two of these kittens were mated, and describe using genetic terminology the characteristics of the offspring.

A The ratio would be 3:1 in favour of long tails. There would be a $^1/_4$ chance of a homozygous dominant individual, a $^2/_4$ chance of a heterozygous individual and $^1/_4$ chance of a homozygous recessive individual.

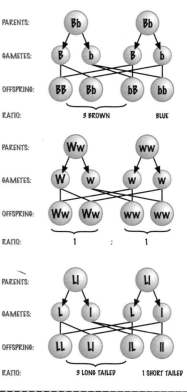

Cystic fibrosis, Huntington's disease and sickle-cell anaemia are three disorders which are inherited.

Cystic Fibrosis – Caused By Recessive Alleles

- Cystic Fibrosis can be passed on by parents, neither of whom have the disorder (ie. they are 'carriers')
- ... if each is carrying just one RECESSIVE allele for the condition.
- It is a disorder of cell membranes causing THICK and STICKY MUCUS ...
- ... especially in the LUNGS, GUT and PANCREAS, which leads to various complications.

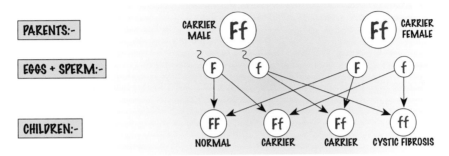

- This particular cross would result in a 1 in 4 chance of producing a sufferer.

Huntington's Disease – Caused By A Dominant Allele

- Huntington's disease, a disorder of the nervous system, is passed on by one parent who has the disorder ...
- ... and therefore is caused by a DOMINANT allele.
- It produces TREMORS, and WRITHING and ultimately can lead to DEMENTIA (loss of sanity).

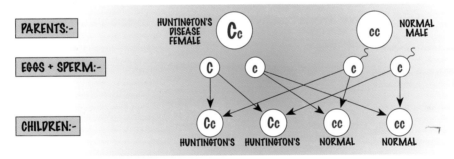

- Here there is a 1 in 2 chance of producing a sufferer.

Sickle-cell Anaemia – Caused By A Recessive Allele

- Sickle-cell anaemia can be passed on by parents neither of whom has the disorder ...
- ... if each is carrying just ONE RECESSIVE ALLELE for the condition.
- Sufferers produce abnormally-shaped red blood cells (SICKLE-SHAPED!), which reduce the oxygen carrying capacity, ...
- ... and they experience general weakness and ANAEMIA.

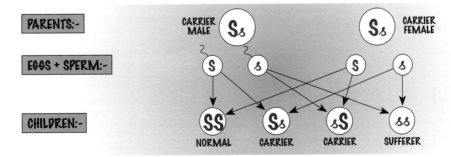

- The HETEROZYGOUS (Ss) INDIVIDUALS also show up to 50% sickling of cells ...
- ... but show an INCREASED RESISTANCE TO MALARIA which is an advantage ...
- ... in areas where MALARIA is prevalent.

Reproducing Plants Artificially

- Plants can reproduce ASEXUALLY ie. without a partner and many do so naturally.
- All the offspring produced ASEXUALLY are CLONES ...
- ... ie. they are GENETICALLY IDENTICAL TO THE PARENT PLANT.

eg. SPIDER PLANT

STOLON - a rooting side branch

NEW INDIVIDUAL ESTABLISHED

NOW INDEPENDENT

TAKING CUTTINGS:

- When a gardener has a plant with all the DESIRED CHARACTERISTICS ...
- ... he may choose to produce lots of them by taking STEM, LEAF or ROOT CUTTINGS ...
- These should be grown in a DAMP ATMOSPHERE until ROOTS DEVELOP.

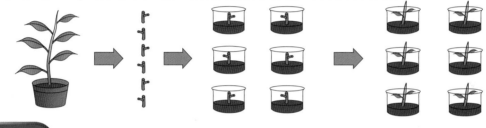

Cloning

CLONES are GENETICALLY IDENTICAL INDIVIDUALS eg. identical twins. So if you've got an organism which is just ideal why not clone thousands of them? This is exactly what's happening in modern agriculture, and this is how ...

1. Taking cuttings ... This is dealt with above.

2. Tissue culture ...

PARENT PLANT - with the characteristics that you want.

A few cells are scraped off into several beakers containing NUTRIENTS AND HORMONES.

A week or two later we've got lots and lots of genetically identical plantlets growing. And we can do the same to these ...

- This whole process must be ASEPTIC (carried out in the ABSENCE OF HARMFUL BACTERIA) ...
  ... otherwise the new plants will ROT.

3. Embryo transplants ... Instead of waiting for normal breeding cycles farmers can obtain many more offspring by using their best animals to produce embryos which can be inserted into 'mother' animals.

PRIZE EWE

PRIZE RAM

PARENTS with desired characteristics are mated.

Embryo is removed before the cells become specialised ...

... then split apart into several clumps.

These embryos are then implanted into the uteruses of sheep who will eventually give birth to clones.

Selective Breeding Down The Ages

Farmers and livestock have been using the principles of selective breeding for hundreds of years without really understanding the genetic basis for it. The simple rule was to keep the best examples of your animals and plants for breeding and to take the rest to market. The same is true of dog breeders who have systematically selected animals which show the desired characteristics and bred them ...

Choose the two spottiest to breed ...and then the spottiest of their offspring ...   to eventually get Dalmations.

Development Of Modern Cattle

In a competitive farming industry, cattle need to be highly efficient at their job if the farm is to make money. Efficiency means specialisation. In other words cattle have been carefully bred to fulfil certain criteria. In general, this means cattle are selectively bred for one of the following characteristics ...

- **QUANTITY OF MILK PRODUCED ...**
  Some cattle are milk specialists. They churn the stuff out at a great rate and we're all very happy about that. This is no coincidence. These are the result of years of breeding good milk producers with other good milk producers to end up with the champions we have now.

Friesian

- **QUALITY OF MILK PRODUCED ...**
  The amount of fat in milk is a sign of its quality and some cows, although perhaps not producing the same volume as other cows, produce lovely creamy, high fat milk. Again, this is down to artificial selection.

Jersey

- **BEEF PRODUCTION ...**
  The characteristics of the Hereford and Angus varieties have been selected over the past 200 years. They include hardiness, early maturity, high numbers of offspring, and the swift efficient conversion of grass into meat.

Hereford

SELECTIVE BREEDING PRODUCES NEW VARIETIES OF ORGANISM	•	SELECTIVE BREEDING PRODUCES ANIMALS AND PLANTS WITH INCREASED YIELDS

	ADVANTAGES	DISADVANTAGES
CLONING	• Allows LARGE NUMBERS of organisms with the DESIRED CHARACTERISTICS to be produced. • EFFICIENT PROCESS that can increase the economic performance of farmers and plant growers.	• Cloning results in a REDUCED NUMBER OF ALLELES in the population. • LOSS OF VARIATION which reduces the species' ability to respond to environmental change. • Reduces the number of alleles available for further selective breeding (see below).
SELECTIVE BREEDING	• Produces an organism with THE RIGHT CHARACTERISTICS for a particular function. • In farming and horticulture produces a MORE EFFICIENT and ECONOMICALLY VIABLE process.	• Intensive selection results in a REDUCED NUMBER OF ALLELES in the population. • LOSS OF VARIATION which reduces the species' ability to respond to environmental change. • Reduces the number of alleles available for further selective breeding.

Reasons For Genetic Modification Of Organisms

Altering the genetic make-up of an organism can be done for many reasons ...

- To improve the crop yield eg. to produce larger tomatoes, potatoes, wheat seed-heads, more oil from oilseed rape etc etc etc.
- To improve resistance to pests or herbicides eg. Pyrethrum is an insecticide prepared from chrysanthemum plants. The actual gene for Pyrethrum can be inserted into soya plants to provide 'in-built' protection against insect damage.
- To extend the shelf-life of fast ripening crops such as tomatoes.
- To harness the cell chemistry of an organism so that it produces a substance that you require, eg. production of human insulin.

All these processes involve transferring genetic material from one organism to another. In the case of both animals and plants genes are often transferred at an early stage of their development so that they develop with desired characteristics. These characteristics can then be passed onto the offspring if the organism reproduces asexually or is cloned.

Genetic Engineering – The Process

Human insulin can be produced by genetic engineering. This is a hormone, produced by the pancreas, which helps to control the level of glucose in the blood. Diabetics can't produce enough insulin and often need to inject it.

STEP 1

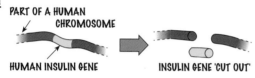

PART OF A HUMAN CHROMOSOME

HUMAN INSULIN GENE

INSULIN GENE 'CUT OUT'

The gene for insulin production is 'cut out' of a human chromosome using RESTRICTION ENZYMES.
These 'cut' DNA at very specific places enabling scientists to remove the precise piece of DNA they want; in this case the gene for insulin production.

STEP 2

Another restriction enzyme is then used to cut open a ring of bacterial DNA (a plasmid). Other enzymes are then used to insert the piece of human DNA into the plasmid. The repaired plasmid is now ready for step 3.

RING OF BACTERIAL DNA CUT OPEN

HUMAN INSULIN GENE INSERTED INTO BACTERIAL DNA

STEP 3

VAT

The plasmid is now reinserted into a bacterium which starts to divide rapidly. As it divides it replicates the plasmid and soon there are millions of them - each with instructions to make insulin.

- When the above process has been completed the bacteria is CULTURED ON A LARGE SCALE ...
- ... and COMMERCIAL QUANTITIES OF INSULIN are then produced.

The Great Genetics Debate

- SCIENTISTS have made GREAT ADVANCES in their understanding of genes and ...
1. ... have IDENTIFIED GENES that control certain characteristics.
2. ... can determine whether a person's genes may lead to them having an INCREASED RISK of CONTRACTING A PARTICULAR ILLNESS eg. breast cancer.
3. ... may soon be able to 'REMOVE' FAULTY GENES and reduce genetic diseases.

- Some parts of society are CONCERNED that ...
1. ... unborn children will be GENETICALLY SCREENED and aborted if their genetic make-up is faulty.
2. ... parents may want to artificially DECIDE ON THE GENETIC MAKE-UP of their child.
3. ... some insurance companies may GENETICALLY SCREEN applicants and refuse to insure people who have an increased genetic risk of an illness or disease. This may prevent these people being able to drive or buy homes due to lack of insurance.

The Theory Of Evolution

The THEORY OF EVOLUTION states...

... that all LIVING THINGS which EXIST TODAY and many more that are now EXTINCT...

... have EVOLVED from simple life forms, which first developed 3,000,000,000 (billion) years ago.

- EVOLUTION is the SLOW, CONTINUAL CHANGE of organisms over a VERY LONG PERIOD...
  ...to become BETTER ADAPTED to their environment.
- If the ENVIRONMENT CHANGES, SPECIES MUST CHANGE with it if they are TO SURVIVE.
- Species which AREN'T ADAPTED to their environment will become EXTINCT.
- A SPECIES is defined as a group of organisms which can freely interbreed to produce FERTILE offspring.

The Reasons For Extinction Of Species

INCREASED COMPETITION

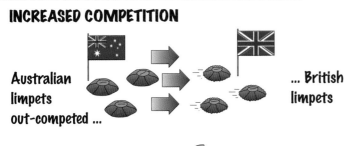

Australian limpets out-competed ...

... British limpets

CHANGE IN THE ENVIRONMENT

ONCE WELL ADAPTED   NOW POORLY ADAPTED

NEW PREDATORS

The Dodo ... hunted by humans and animals introduced by humans.

NEW DISEASES

The Fossil Record

FOSSILS are the 'REMAINS' of PLANTS OR ANIMALS from many years ago which are found in rock.

Fossils can be formed in various ways ...
- From the hard parts of animals that do not decay easily.
- From parts of animals and plants which have not decayed because one or more of the conditions needed for decay were absent eg. oxygen, moisture, temperature or correct pH.
- Also the soft parts of organisms can be replaced by minerals as they decay. This can preserve the traces of footprints, burrows or rootlets.

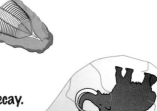

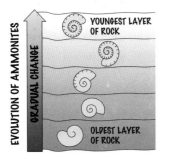

- If we look at exposed rock strata, ...
- ... it is possible to follow the GRADUAL CHANGES which have taken place in an organism over time.
- Even though the fossil record is incomplete, these gradual changes confirm that ...
- ... SPECIES HAVE CHANGED OVER LONG PERIODS OF TIME ...
- ... providing STRONG EVIDENCE FOR EVOLUTION.

Charles Darwin

He made four very important observations ...
- All living things produce far more offspring than actually survive to adulthood.
- In spite of this, population sizes remain fairly constant, all things being equal.
- There is variation in members of the same species.
- Characteristics can be passed on from one generation to the next.
  From these observations Darwin deduced that all organisms were involved in a struggle for survival in which only the best adapted organisms would survive, reproduce and pass on their characteristics. This formed the basis for his famous theory of 'Evolution by Natural Selection'.
- The reaction, particularly from religious authorities, was hostile to Darwin's theory since they felt he was saying that 'men were descended from monkeys' (which he wasn't) and that he was denying God's role in the creation of man. This meant that his theory was only slowly and reluctantly accepted by many people in spite of the great number of eminent supporters he had.

Evolution By Natural Selection

Evolution is the CHANGE IN A POPULATION over a large number of generations that may result in THE FORMATION OF A NEW SPECIES, the members of which are BETTER ADAPTED TO THEIR ENVIRONMENT.
There are 4 key points to remember:-
1. Individuals within a population show VARIATION (ie. differences due to their genes).
2. There is COMPETITION between individuals for food and mates etc., and also predation and disease. This keeps population sizes constant in spite of the production of many offspring, ie. there is a 'struggle for survival', and many individuals die.
3. Individuals which are BETTER ADAPTED to the environment are more likely to survive, breed successfully and produce offspring. This is termed 'SURVIVAL OF THE FITTEST'.
4. These 'survivors' will therefore PASS ON THEIR GENES to these offspring resulting in an improved organism being evolved through NATURAL SELECTION.

VARIATION and COMPETITION ensure BETTER ADAPTED organisms PASS ON THEIR GENES

Penicillin-resistant Bacteria

This is an increasing problem and is caused by a mutation in the bacteria which confers resistance to penicillin. Consequently non-resistant bacteria are killed off leaving the field free for the resistant ones to reproduce passing on their resistance. This is why doctors are reluctant to prescribe antibiotics when the patient can do without them.

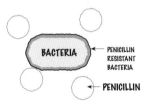

VARIATION	COMPETITION	BEST ADAPTED	PASS ON THEIR GENES
Bacteria MUTATED. Some were resistant to the ANTIBIOTIC PENICILLIN others were not.	The non-resistant bacteria were more likely to be killed by the penicillin.	The PENICILLIN-RESISTANT bacteria survived and reproduced more often.	More bacteria are becoming resistant to penicillin. This is a major health issue.

HIGHER TIER

Conflicting Theories Of Evolution

JEAN BAPTISTE DE LAMARCK (1744-1829) was the first SCIENTIST to try to explain the 'VARIETY OF LIFE'.
- He suggested that an ORGANISM CHANGED to become MORE ADAPTED to its environment.
- For example, a GIRAFFE'S LONG NECK was caused by it STRETCHING TO REACH LEAVES. The longer neck was then passed onto its offspring. Or, that if you kept cutting off the tails of mice for generation after generation they would eventually lose their tails.
- Other scientists believed that God individually created all the different species including those extinct forms found in the fossil record.
- Even now there are many people who do not accept Darwin's theory although it must be said that this is usually based on religious rather than scientific grounds.

VARIATION, DNA AND MUTATIONS

VARIATION describes differences between individuals of the same species, and is due to a combination of GENETIC AND ENVIRONMENTAL CAUSES.
- SEXUAL reproduction causes lots of variation.
- ASEXUAL reproduction causes no variation (ie. clones)

THE NATURE OF THE GENE
- A gene is a section of DNA which determines a particular inherited characteristic eg. blue eyes.
- Different forms of gene are called ALLELES. New forms of genes can arise through MUTATION. Mutation frequency is caused by U-V light, X-rays, radioactive substances and certain chemicals.

CAUSES	EFFECTS
• Mutations occur naturally but ...	• Most mutations are HARMFUL and in ...
• ... there is an increased risk of mutation if ...	• ... REPRODUCTIVE CELLS can cause DEATH or ABNORMALITY.
• individuals are exposed to MUTAGENIC AGENTS ...	• In BODY CELLS they may cause CANCER.
• ... eg. IONISING RADIATION (inc. U-V LIGHT, X-RAYS) ...	• Some mutations are NEUTRAL, and in RARE CASES ...
• ... RADIOACTIVE SUBSTANCES and CERTAIN CHEMICALS.	• ... may INCREASE THE SURVIVAL CHANCES OF AN ORGANISM ...
• THE GREATER THE DOSE, THE GREATER THE RISK.	• ... and its OFFSPRING WHO INHERIT THE GENE.

The 4 bases in the DNA molecule act as a code for the 20 amino acids we need to make protein. A section of DNA therefore instructs the sequence for a particular protein.

A GENE

3 bases code for one amino acid

CELL DIVISION, SEX CHROMOSOMES AND MENDEL

CELL DIVISION

MEIOSIS ← → MITOSIS

- MEIOSIS - Reproductive cell division which halves the chromosome number.
- MITOSIS - Normal cell division which maintains the number of chromosomes.

Sexual reproduction promotes variation because: MEIOSIS shuffles the genes, gametes fuse RANDOMLY; and alleles in a pair may be different.

INHERITANCE OF SEX (SEX CHROMOSOMES)
Half the sperms carry an X chromosome, the other half carry a Y chromosome. All the eggs carry X chromosomes. XX = GIRL XY = BOY.

X Y X

XX — GIRL
XY — BOY

GREGOR MENDEL
Tall x Dwarf produced only Tall plants. Mendel said:
1. 'When pure-breeding plants with contrasting traits are crossed all offspring will resemble ONE of the parents'. When two of these Tall plants were then crossed, they produced a 3:1 ratio of Tall to Dwarf plants.
2. 'For each trait every individual must have TWO determiners'. By these he meant genes.

3:1

TERMINOLOGY AND INHERITED DISORDERS

TERMINOLOGY ... ALLELE - An alternative form of a gene eg. brown/blue eyes.
DOMINANT - An allele which expresses itself when present on only one of the chromosomes of a pair.
RECESSIVE - An allele which expresses itself only when a dominant allele is not present.

HOMOZYGOUS - Both chromosomes contain the same allele eg. BB.
HETEROZYGOUS - Both chromosomes contain different alleles eg. Bb.

INHERITED DISORDERS AS EXAMPLES OF MONOHYBRID INHERITANCE

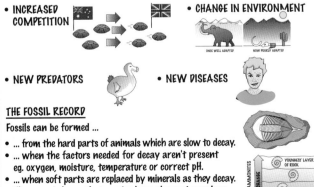

CYSTIC FIBROSIS   HUNTINGTON'S DISEASE

SICKLE-CELL ANAEMIA

CYSTIC FIBROSIS causes too much mucus in lungs, gut and pancreas.
HUNTINGTON'S causes tremors and writhing and can lead to dementia.
SICKLE-CELL ANAEMIA causes weakness and anaemia. Carriers are resistant to malaria.

CLONING, SELECTION AND GENETIC MODIFICATION

CLONING
- Clones are GENETICALLY IDENTICAL INDIVIDUALS.
- Taking cuttings, tissue culture and embryo transplants all produce clones.
- Results in a reduction in the number of alleles in a population.

ARTIFICIAL SELECTION or selective breeding means breeding the 'best' to the 'best' and retaining the 'best' offspring. This principle has been used to ...
- Increase the quality and quantity of milk produced by cattle.
- Increase the quality and quantity of beef.

GENETIC ENGINEERING
This can be used to improve crop yield, improve disease resistance, extend shelf-life, to harness the cell chemistry in order to produce something eg. insulin.

INSULIN PRODUCTION ...
- Restriction enzymes are used to cut and place the gene. In this case human insulin is manufactured.

PROS AND CONS
- Information can help to predict and therefore prevent many illnesses and conditions, so benefiting the human race.
- The information may be used to discriminate against people and also to manipulate the characteristics of unborn babies.

EXTINCTION AND THE FOSSIL RECORD

Evolution is the slow continual change of organisms over long periods of time so that they become better adapted to their environment. Species which aren't adapted to their environment will become extinct.

REASONS FOR EXTINCTION OF SPECIES

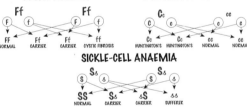

- INCREASED COMPETITION
- CHANGE IN ENVIRONMENT
ONCE WELL ADAPTED   NOW POORLY ADAPTED
- NEW PREDATORS
- NEW DISEASES

THE FOSSIL RECORD
Fossils can be formed ...
- ... from the hard parts of animals which are slow to decay.
- ... when the factors needed for decay aren't present eg. oxygen, moisture, temperature or correct pH.
- ... when soft parts are replaced by minerals as they decay. The record shows that species have changed over long periods of time, and these changes are visible in the rock strata. This is strong evidence for evolution.

EVOLUTION OF AMMONITES

YOUNGEST LAYER OF ROCK

GRADUAL CHANGE

OLDEST LAYER OF ROCK

EVOLUTION BY NATURAL SELECTION

Charles Darwin made observations which enabled him to deduce that all organisms are involved in a struggle for survival in which only the best adapted organisms would survive, reproduce and pass on their characteristics ...

EVOLUTION BY NATURAL SELECTION
- In all populations there is VARIATION.
- There is always COMPETITION for food and mates and this keeps population sizes constant in spite of many offspring.
- The BETTER ADAPTED individuals will be able to produce the most offspring.
- These 'survivors' will PASS ON THEIR GENES which made them better adapted individuals, resulting in evolution.

PENICILLIN-RESISTANT BACTERIA

VARIATION	COMPETITION	BEST ADAPTED	PASS ON THEIR GENES
Bacteria MUTATED. Some were resistant to the ANTIBIOTIC PENICILLIN others were not.	The non-resistant bacteria were more likely to be killed by the penicillin.	The PENICILLIN-RESISTANT bacteria survived and reproduced more often.	More bacteria are becoming resistant to penicillin. This is a major health issue.

CONFLICTING THEORIES OF EVOLUTION
LAMARCK suggested that organisms changed to become adapted to their environment eg. a giraffe got a long neck through stretching and this could be passed on!!

1. a) Tom and Joe are identical twins. Look at the features listed and say which you would expect to be identical.
   HEIGHT, WEIGHT, INTELLIGENCE, SHOE SIZE, RUNNING SPEED, EYE COLOUR, FINGER PRINTS.
   b) Explain why some of these features are identical.
   c) Explain why some of these features are <u>not</u> identical.

2. a) In simple terms, what do we mean by a gene?
   b) What are chromosomes?
   c) How many chromosomes are found in human skin cells?

3. a) Explain the main differences between sexual and asexual reproduction.
   b) What effect do these two types of reproduction have on variation?

4. a) Which type of cell division has the following features ...
   CHROMOSOME REPLICATION, ONE CELL DIVISION, MAINTENANCE OF CHROMOSOME NUMBER?
   b) Where does this type of cell division occur?
   c) Which type of cell division has the following features ...
   CHROMOSOME REPLICATION, TWO CELL DIVISIONS, HALVING OF CHROMOSOME NUMBER?
   d) Where does this type of cell division occur?

5. Why does sexual reproduction promote variation?

6. The strands of a DNA molecule are linked by a series of paired bases.
   a) Why are these paired bases important?
   b) How many pairs of bases represent one amino acid?

7. a) What are mutations?
   b) List three factors which may cause an increased risk of mutation.
   c) What effects can mutations have on an individual?

8. a) What are the female sex chromosomes called?
   b) What are the male sex chromosomes called?
   c) Draw a genetic diagram to illustrate the inheritance of sex.
   d) What ultimately decides the sex of an individual?

9. Describe the work Gregor Mendel carried out using pea plants and explain why the results he obtained marks the start of modern genetics.

11. What is the difference between a dominant and a recessive allele?

12. a) A certain type of mouse has two alleles which control the colour of its fur. Brown fur is dominant to black fur.

    Using the letters 'B', and 'b', describe the following conditions ...

    Heterozygous, Homozygous dominant, a black mouse.

    b) Draw a genetic diagram to illustrate a cross between a heterozygous individual and an individual with black fur.

13. a) Describe the symptoms of Cystic Fibrosis.

    b) Draw a genetic diagram to illustrate a cross between two carriers for the disease.

14. a) Describe the symptoms of Huntington's disease.

    b) Draw a genetic diagram to illustrate a cross between a sufferer and a normal individual.

15. a) Describe the symptoms of sickle-cell anaemia.

    b) Draw a genetic diagram to illustrate a cross between two carriers of the disease.

16. a) Why is it economic good sense for a gardener to take cuttings?

    b) What disadvantage is there in this method of producing new plants?

    c) Farmers and breeders use selective breeding for two reasons. What are these reasons?

17. a) Describe how tissue culture and embryo transplants can be used to obtain more offspring in a shorter time.

    b) What is the main disadvantage of using intensive selection methods to produce desirable characteristics?

18. Describe in detail how genetic engineering has been used on a large scale to help humans.

19. a) What effect might a change of environment have on a species over long periods of time?

    b) What effect might increased competition have on a species?

    c) Name two other factors which could influence the numbers in a population.

20. a) What are fossils?

    b) Describe in detail three methods of fossil formation.

    c) Why do fossils provide strong evidence for evolution?

21. a) List the four principles upon which the theory of evolution by natural selection is based.

    b) Why are doctors reluctant to prescribe antibiotics when the patient can do without them?

    c) Explain Lamarck's theory of evolution.

    d) Explain briefly how this theory could explain the evolution of long necks in giraffes.

- ADAPTATIONS are SPECIAL FEATURES OR BEHAVIOUR which make an organism...
  ...ESPECIALLY WELL-SUITED TO ITS ENVIRONMENT.

- ADAPTATIONS are part of the EVOLUTIONARY PROCESS which 'shapes life' so that a habitat is populated by organisms which excel there. Adaptations increase an organism's chance of survival; they are 'biological solutions' to an environmental challenge!

Examples Of How Organisms Are Adapted To Their Environment

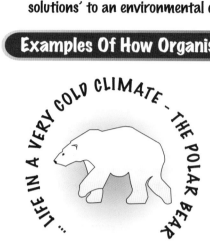

LIFE IN A VERY COLD CLIMATE - THE POLAR BEAR ...

- Rounded shape means a SMALL SURFACE AREA/VOLUME RATIO to REDUCE HEAT LOSS.
- LARGE AMOUNT OF INSULATING FAT beneath the skin, which also acts as a food store.
- THICK GREASY FUR TO ADD TO INSULATION against the cold, and to repel water.
- WHITE COAT so that it is CAMOUFLAGED.
- LARGE FEET to spread its weight on the ice.
- POWERFUL SWIMMER so that it can CATCH ITS FOOD.
- HIBERNATES in the worst weather.

LIFE IN A VERY HOT CLIMATE - THE CAMEL ...

- Long, thin legs and neck means a LARGE SURFACE AREA/VOLUME RATIO to INCREASE HEAT LOSS.
- BODY FAT STORED IN HUMP with almost none beneath the skin, means that heat can be lost quickly through the skin.
- SANDY BROWN COAT to CAMOUFLAGE it in the desert.
- LOSES VERY LITTLE WATER through sweating or in urine.
- CAN DRINK UP TO 20 GALLONS OF WATER in one go.

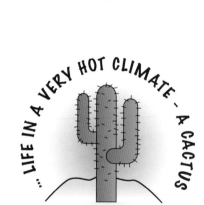

LIFE IN A VERY HOT CLIMATE - A CACTUS ...

- No leaves and a compact shape means a SMALL SURFACE AREA/VOLUME RATIO to REDUCE WATER LOSS.
- THICK, WAXY SURFACE to REDUCE WATER LOSS.
- STORES WATER in spongy layer inside its stem.
- SPINES PROTECT THE CACTI from predators who would 'steal' the CACTI'S WATER STORE.
- STOMATA ONLY OPEN AT NIGHT to REDUCE THE AMOUNT OF WATER LOST.
- Some cacti have SHALLOW SPREADING ROOTS ...
  ... to ABSORB SURFACE WATER whilst others have ...
  ... DEEP ROOTS to tap into underground supplies of water.

LIFE IN AN AQUATIC (WATERY) ENVIRONMENT - THE FISH ...

- Fish are STREAMLINED in shape to allow them to TRAVEL QUICKLY through the water.
- They possess GILLS that can obtain DISSOLVED OXYGEN FROM THE WATER.
- GILLS have a LARGE SURFACE AREA which INCREASE THE AREA over which OXYGEN CAN BE ABSORBED.

Competition

Organisms compete with each other for ...

Plants need light and room to spread leaves. ← **SPACE** → Animals need space to breed and 'rest'. Also territory to hunt in.

Plants absorb nutrients from the soil and compete for light for photosynthesis. ← **FOOD** → Herbivores compete for vegetation, and carnivores compete for their prey.

All plants must absorb water by their roots. ← **WATER** → All animals need water in order to survive.

- In addition to competing for the three factors above, animal populations are also affected by PREDATORS, DISEASE and MIGRATION.
- Plant populations are also affected by grazing by HERBIVORES and disease.
- Remember, when we talk about populations here we mean the total number of individuals of the same species which live in a certain area eg. the number of field mice in a meadow. A community is all the organisms in a particular area ie. many populations of plants and animals.

- When two or more organisms compete in a particular area or habitat, the ORGANISMS WHICH ARE BETTER ADAPTED TO THE ENVIRONMENT ARE MORE SUCCESSFUL and usually exist in larger numbers - often resulting in the complete exclusion of the other competing organisms.

In your examination you may be asked to suggest the factors for which organisms are competing in a given habitat.

Predator/Prey Cycles

- Predators are animals that kill and eat other animals while ...
- ... the animals that are eaten are called the prey.
- Within a natural environment there is a delicate balance ...
- ... between the population of the predator and its prey.

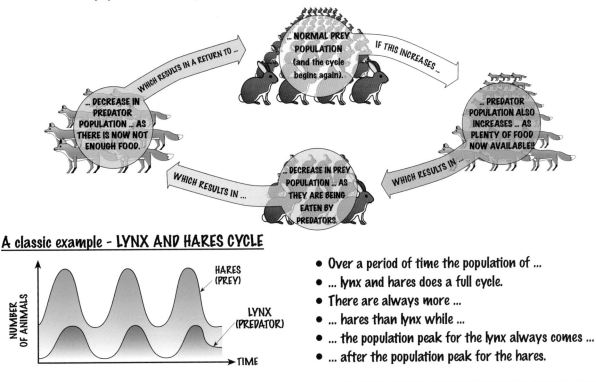

... NORMAL PREY POPULATION (and the cycle begins again).

IF THIS INCREASES ...

... PREDATOR POPULATION ALSO INCREASES ... AS PLENTY OF FOOD NOW AVAILABLE!!

WHICH RESULTS IN ...

... DECREASE IN PREY POPULATION ... AS THEY ARE BEING EATEN BY PREDATORS.

WHICH RESULTS IN ...

... DECREASE IN PREDATOR POPULATION ... AS THERE IS NOW NOT ENOUGH FOOD.

WHICH RESULTS IN A RETURN TO ...

A classic example - LYNX AND HARES CYCLE

NUMBER OF ANIMALS / TIME

HARES (PREY)

LYNX (PREDATOR)

- Over a period of time the population of ...
- ... lynx and hares does a full cycle.
- There are always more ...
- ... hares than lynx while ...
- ... the population peak for the lynx always comes ...
- ... after the population peak for the hares.

NB THE ABOVE GRAPH WOULD BE VERY SIMILAR FOR **ANY** PREDATOR AND PREY POPULATION CYCLE.

Pyramids Of Biomass

Radiation from the sun is the source of energy for all communities of living organisms. Green plants capture a small fraction of the solar energy which reaches them, in the process of photosynthesis. This energy is stored in the substances which make up the cells of the plant and can be passed onto organisms which eat the plant. This transfer of energy can be represented by a food chain ...

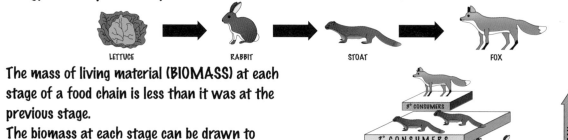

LETTUCE → RABBIT → STOAT → FOX

- The mass of living material (BIOMASS) at each stage of a food chain is less than it was at the previous stage.
- The biomass at each stage can be drawn to scale and shown as a PYRAMID OF BIOMASS.

FOX
STOATS
RABBITS
LETTUCES

PRODUCERS / 1° CONSUMERS / 2° CONSUMERS / 3° CONSUMERS

FLOW OF ENERGY

Because both biomass and energy are lost at each stage of a food chain, it follows that the efficiency of food production can be improved by reducing the number of stages in food chains eg. ...

GRASS → COW → HUMAN   IS NOT AS EFFICIENT AS ...   VARIOUS CROPS → HUMAN

HIGHER TIER

Transfer Of Energy And Biomass

- Biomass and energy are lost at every stage of a food chain because ...
- ... materials and energy are lost in an organism's <u>faeces (waste)</u>, and ...
- ... energy is 'lost' as <u>movement energy</u> and <u>'waste' heat energy</u> originally provided by respiration.
- This last statement is particularly true of warm-blooded animals (birds and mammals).

- The fox gets the last tiny bit of energy and biomass that is left.
- Stoats run, mate, excrete, keep warm and pass on only $\frac{1}{10}$th of the energy they got from the rabbits. A lot of biomass is lost as faeces.
- Rabbits run, mate, excrete, keep warm and pass on only $\frac{1}{10}$th of the energy they got from the lettuce. A lot of biomass is lost in droppings (faeces).
- Only a fraction of the sun's energy is captured. Much of the biomass remains in the root system.

Improving The Efficiency Of Food Production

Since the loss of energy and biomass is due mainly to HEAT LOSS, WASTE and MOVEMENT, it follows that we can improve the efficiency of food production by ...

Limiting an animal's movement, and controlling its temperature.

More of the food eaten by the animal is converted into biomass ... ... because less energy is 'lost' through heat and movement.

Many people feel that this way of rearing animals is unacceptable.

- In plants, efficiency can be improved by USING HORMONES to regulate the ripening of fruits, both on the plant and during transport to consumers.

Recycling The Materials Of Life

- Living things remove materials from the environment for growth and other processes, ...
- ... but when these organisms excrete waste or die, these materials are returned to the environment.
- The key to all this are the MICROORGANISMS...
   ... which break down the WASTE and ...
   ... the DEAD BODIES so that they can ...
   ... be absorbed and used by plants ...
   ... for GROWTH.

> MICROORGANISMS digest materials faster in ...
> ... WARM, MOIST CONDITIONS where ...
> ... there is plenty of OXYGEN.

EATING   WASTE   DEATH   ABSORPTION

BROKEN DOWN BY
MICROORGANISMS

Humans also quite deliberately use MICROORGANISMS ...

1. AT SEWAGE WORKS ...	2. IN COMPOST HEAPS ...
● ... to break down HUMAN WASTE.	● ... to break down PLANT MATERIAL WASTE.

The Carbon Cycle

In a stable community, the processes which remove materials ...
... are balanced by processes which return materials. A sort of constant recycling.
The constant recycling of carbon is called the Carbon Cycle.

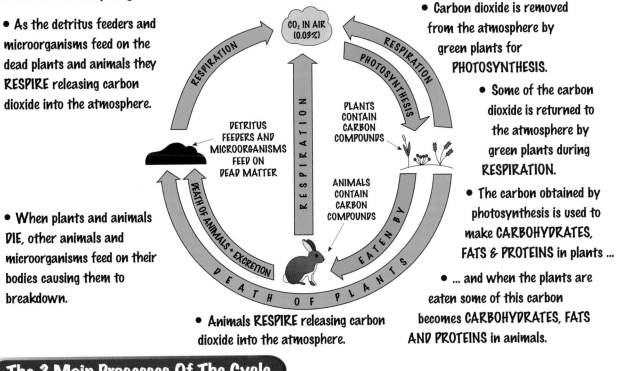

- As the detritus feeders and microorganisms feed on the dead plants and animals they RESPIRE releasing carbon dioxide into the atmosphere.

- When plants and animals DIE, other animals and microorganisms feed on their bodies causing them to breakdown.

CO₂ IN AIR (0.03%)

RESPIRATION   RESPIRATION   PHOTOSYNTHESIS

PLANTS CONTAIN CARBON COMPOUNDS

DETRITUS FEEDERS AND MICROORGANISMS FEED ON DEAD MATTER

RESPIRATION

ANIMALS CONTAIN CARBON COMPOUNDS

DEATH OF ANIMALS + EXCRETION   EATEN BY PLANTS   DEATH OF PLANTS

- Carbon dioxide is removed from the atmosphere by green plants for PHOTOSYNTHESIS.

  - Some of the carbon dioxide is returned to the atmosphere by green plants during RESPIRATION.

  - The carbon obtained by photosynthesis is used to make CARBOHYDRATES, FATS & PROTEINS in plants ...

  - ... and when the plants are eaten some of this carbon becomes CARBOHYDRATES, FATS AND PROTEINS in animals.

- Animals RESPIRE releasing carbon dioxide into the atmosphere.

The 3 Main Processes Of The Cycle

1. PHOTOSYNTHESIS	2. RESPIRATION	3. TRANSFER OF CARBON
● CO₂ taken up ... ● ... by PLANTS ... ● ... to produce GLUCOSE.	● CO₂ given out ... ● ... by PLANTS, ANIMALS ... ● ... and MICROORGANISMS during decay process.	● CARBON from CO₂ is used to make ... ... CARBOHYDRATES, FATS and PROTEINS within the PLANT. ● TRANSFER of CARBON from PLANT to ANIMAL when PLANT IS EATEN. ● Further transfer when these animals are eaten by OTHER animals.

The Nitrogen Cycle

● Besides carbon, nitrogen is also constantly recycled ...

● ... this cycle, naturally enough, is called the Nitrogen Cycle and involves the following stages ...

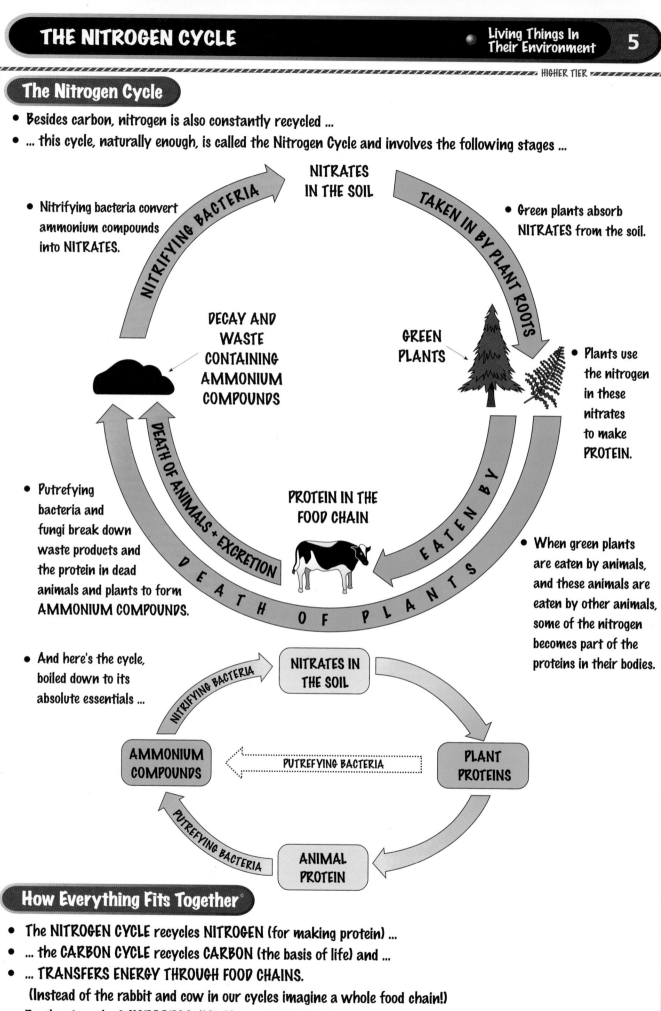

NITRATES IN THE SOIL

NITRIFYING BACTERIA

TAKEN IN BY PLANT ROOTS

● Nitrifying bacteria convert ammonium compounds into NITRATES.

● Green plants absorb NITRATES from the soil.

GREEN PLANTS

DECAY AND WASTE CONTAINING AMMONIUM COMPOUNDS

● Plants use the nitrogen in these nitrates to make PROTEIN.

DEATH OF ANIMALS + EXCRETION

● Putrefying bacteria and fungi break down waste products and the protein in dead animals and plants to form AMMONIUM COMPOUNDS.

PROTEIN IN THE FOOD CHAIN

EATEN BY

DEATH OF PLANTS

● When green plants are eaten by animals, and these animals are eaten by other animals, some of the nitrogen becomes part of the proteins in their bodies.

● And here's the cycle, boiled down to its absolute essentials ...

NITRATES IN THE SOIL

NITRIFYING BACTERIA

AMMONIUM COMPOUNDS

PUTREFYING BACTERIA

PLANT PROTEINS

PUTREFYING BACTERIA

ANIMAL PROTEIN

How Everything Fits Together

● The NITROGEN CYCLE recycles NITROGEN (for making protein) ...

● ... the CARBON CYCLE recycles CARBON (the basis of life) and ...

● ... TRANSFERS ENERGY THROUGH FOOD CHAINS.
(Instead of the rabbit and cow in our cycles imagine a whole food chain!)

● By the time the MICROORGANISMS and DETRITUS FEEDERS have broken down the waste and dead bodies ...
... all the ENERGY CAPTURED BY GREEN PLANTS HAS BEEN TRANSFERRED.

The Population Explosion

The HUMAN POPULATION is INCREASING EXPONENTIALLY, and the standard of living of most people has improved enormously over the past 50 years. This causes the following major problems ...

- Raw materials, including non-renewable energy resources are rapidly being used up.
- Reduction in the amount of land available for other animals and plants (see diagram).
- Increasingly more waste is being produced.
- Improper handling of this waste is leading to an increase in environmental pollution.

HUMAN POPULATION

EXPONENTIAL INCREASE

TIME

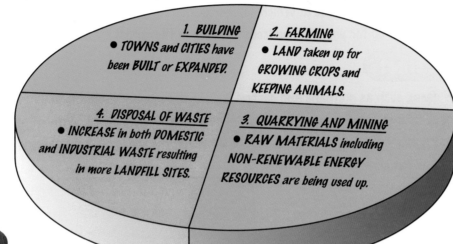

1. BUILDING
- TOWNS and CITIES have been BUILT or EXPANDED.

2. FARMING
- LAND taken up for GROWING CROPS and KEEPING ANIMALS.

4. DISPOSAL OF WASTE
- INCREASE in both DOMESTIC and INDUSTRIAL WASTE resulting in more LANDFILL SITES.

3. QUARRYING AND MINING
- RAW MATERIALS including NON-RENEWABLE ENERGY RESOURCES are being used up.

Pollution

Human activities may pollute:

WATER - with sewage, fertiliser or toxic chemicals.

AIR - with smoke and gases such as carbon dioxide, sulphur dioxide and oxides of nitrogen.

LAND - with toxic chemicals such as pesticides and herbicides, which may be washed from land into water.

- Unless waste is properly handled and stored more pollution will be caused.

Acid Rain

When fossil fuels are burned CARBON DIOXIDE is released into the atmosphere. SULPHUR DIOXIDE and NITROGEN OXIDES are also released from ...

● INDUSTRY ● POWER STATIONS ● MOTOR VEHICLE EXHAUSTS

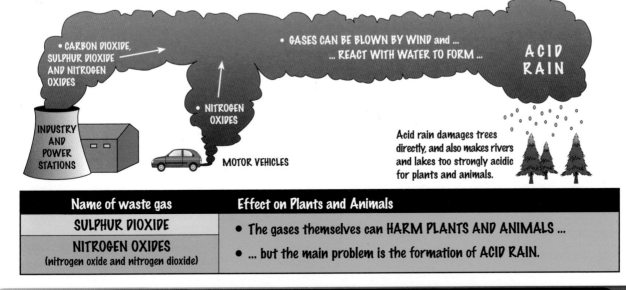

- CARBON DIOXIDE, SULPHUR DIOXIDE AND NITROGEN OXIDES

- GASES CAN BE BLOWN BY WIND and ...
  ... REACT WITH WATER TO FORM ...

ACID RAIN

- NITROGEN OXIDES

INDUSTRY AND POWER STATIONS

MOTOR VEHICLES

Acid rain damages trees directly, and also makes rivers and lakes too strongly acidic for plants and animals.

Name of waste gas	Effect on Plants and Animals
SULPHUR DIOXIDE	- The gases themselves can HARM PLANTS AND ANIMALS ...
NITROGEN OXIDES (nitrogen oxide and nitrogen dioxide)	- ... but the main problem is the formation of ACID RAIN.

Deforestation

Deforestation involves the large scale cutting down of trees for timber, and to provide land for agricultural use.

This has occurred in many tropical areas with devastating consequences for the environment ...

- Deforestation has increased the release of CO_2 into the atmosphere due to burning of the wood and also as a result of the decay of the wood by microorganisms.
- Deforestation has also reduced the rate at which carbon dioxide is removed from the atmosphere by photosynthesis and locked up for possibly hundreds of years in the actual structure of the wood.

The Greenhouse Effect

This describes how gases, such as methane and carbon dioxide, act like an insulating blanket by preventing a substantial amount of heat energy 'escaping' from the Earth's surface into space. Without any such effect the Earth would be a far colder and quite inhospitable place. However, the levels of these gases are slowly rising and so too is the overall temperature of the planet.

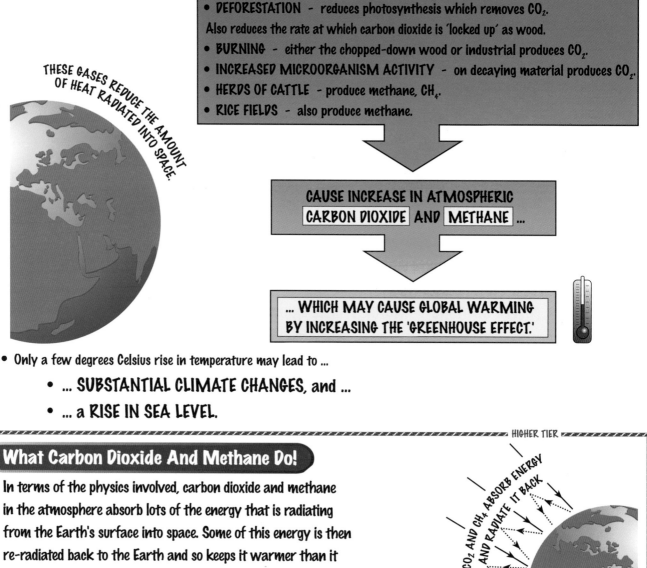

THESE GASES REDUCE THE AMOUNT OF HEAT RADIATED INTO SPACE.

- DEFORESTATION - reduces photosynthesis which removes CO_2. Also reduces the rate at which carbon dioxide is 'locked up' as wood.
- BURNING - either the chopped-down wood or industrial produces CO_2.
- INCREASED MICROORGANISM ACTIVITY - on decaying material produces CO_2.
- HERDS OF CATTLE - produce methane, CH_4.
- RICE FIELDS - also produce methane.

CAUSE INCREASE IN ATMOSPHERIC CARBON DIOXIDE AND METHANE ...

... WHICH MAY CAUSE GLOBAL WARMING BY INCREASING THE 'GREENHOUSE EFFECT.'

- Only a few degrees Celsius rise in temperature may lead to ...
  - ... SUBSTANTIAL CLIMATE CHANGES, and ...
  - ... a RISE IN SEA LEVEL.

HIGHER TIER

What Carbon Dioxide And Methane Do!

In terms of the physics involved, carbon dioxide and methane in the atmosphere absorb lots of the energy that is radiating from the Earth's surface into space. Some of this energy is then re-radiated back to the Earth and so keeps it warmer than it would otherwise be.

CO_2 AND CH_4 ABSORB ENERGY AND RADIATE IT BACK

This is the process whereby stretches of water can become stagnant very quickly due to a sequence of events started by carelessness in the overuse of fertiliser.

There are 6 stages:-

1. **INORGANIC FERTILISERS** ... used by farmers may be washed into lakes and rivers. The fertiliser is originally sprayed onto crops to replace the nutrients which previous crops remove.

2. **GROWTH** ... of water plants caused by this fertiliser, happens rapidly. The nitrogen in particular is taken up quickly by the plants and used to make protein for growth of new and existing shoots.

3. **DEATH** ... of some of these plants due to lack of light from over-crowding. The plants literally choke themselves to death as they try to gain sufficient light from the sun, and more nutrients from the water.

4. **MICROORGANISMS** ... which feed on dead organisms now increase massively in number. These are the putrefying bacteria which breakdown dead organic material via respiration, and release simpler substances for recycling.

5. **OXYGEN** ... is used up quickly by this huge number of microorganisms. The process of breakdown is respiration ie. the microorganisms respire the organic material and need oxygen to do so.

6. **SUFFOCATION** ... of fishes and other aquatic animals due to lack of oxygen in the water. Eventually virtually all the oxygen is removed from the water leaving insufficient for larger organisms.

UNTREATED SEWAGE HAS THE SAME EFFECT AS EXCESS FERTILISER.

- SUSTAINABLE DEVELOPMENT is concerned with three related issues ...
  - ECONOMIC DEVELOPMENT
  - SOCIAL DEVELOPMENT
  - ENVIRONMENTAL PROTECTION

- The UNITED NATIONS EARTH SUMMIT in Rio de Janeiro in 1992 ...
  ... was arguably the MAJOR EVENT in producing a coordinated WORLDWIDE effort ...
  ... to produce sustained ECONOMIC and SOCIAL DEVELOPMENT ...
  ... that would benefit ALL the WORLD'S PEOPLE, particularly the poor ...
  ... whilst BALANCING the need to protect the environment by REDUCING POLLUTION and ensuring
     SUSTAINABLE RESOURCES.

- SUSTAINABLE RESOURCES are resources that can be maintained in the LONG TERM at a level that allows
  APPROPRIATE CONSUMPTION or USE by people ...
  ... this often requires LIMITING EXPLOITATION by using QUOTAS or ...
  ... ensuring the resources are REPLENISHED or RESTOCKED.

Example 1 - Cod in the North Sea

- In the mid-1970's fish stocks in the North Sea dwindled due to OVERFISHING.
- Nations proposed various measures to remedy the situation, including ...
- ... imposing FISHING QUOTAS by limiting the catch a vessel was allowed to land over a certain period of time.
- ... limiting the mesh size of nets so that YOUNGER FISH weren't caught before they reached BREEDING AGE.

Example 2 - Pine forests in Scandinavia

- Scandinavia uses a lot of pine wood to make furniture, paper and provide energy.
- To ensure the long-term economic viability of pine-related industries ...
- ... companies REPLENISH and RESTOCK THE PINE FORESTS ...
- ... by planting a NEW SAPLING for each mature tree cut down.

Endangered Species

- When COUNTRIES or COMPANIES neglect the ideas of sustainable development ...
  ... various species can become endangered.

- The RED KITE was exploited ...
  ... for its feathers.
- The OSPREY numbers reduced ...
  ... as its habitats were destroyed
- The RED SQUIRREL was endangered ...
  ... with the introduction of the grey squirrel.

- Many ENDANGERED SPECIES are now PROTECTED ...
  ... the COUNTRYSIDE COUNCIL FOR WALES provides LEGAL PROTECTION for red squirrels who cannot be trapped,
  killed or kept except under special licence ...
  ... the red kite and osprey both have PROTECTED SITES in Wales where they can live and breed undisturbed.
- EDUCATION has become a powerful 'weapon' in ...
  ... protecting endangered species and promoting the ideas behind sustainable development.

ADAPTATIONS AND POPULATIONS

Adaptations are special features or behaviours which make an organism especially well suited to its environment, and therefore better able to compete with other organisms.

LIFE IN A VERY HOT CLIMATE ... THE CAMEL
- Large SA/VOL ratio
- Fat in hump
- Brown Fur
- Little water lost through sweating or urine.
- Drinks 20 gals in one go!

LIFE IN A VERY HOT CLIMATE ... A CACTUS
- Small SA/VOL ratio
- Thick waxy surface
- Stores water
- Spines
- Stomata open at night
- Special root systems

LIFE IN A VERY COLD CLIMATE ... THE POLAR BEAR
- Small SA/VOL ratio
- Fat beneath skin
- White fur
- Greasy fur
- Large feet
- Hibernation

COMPETITION

Organisms compete for SPACE, FOOD and WATER. The size of a population may also be influenced by ...

Food/nutrients available, competition for food/nutrients, competition for light, predation, grazing and disease.

PREDATORS AND PREY

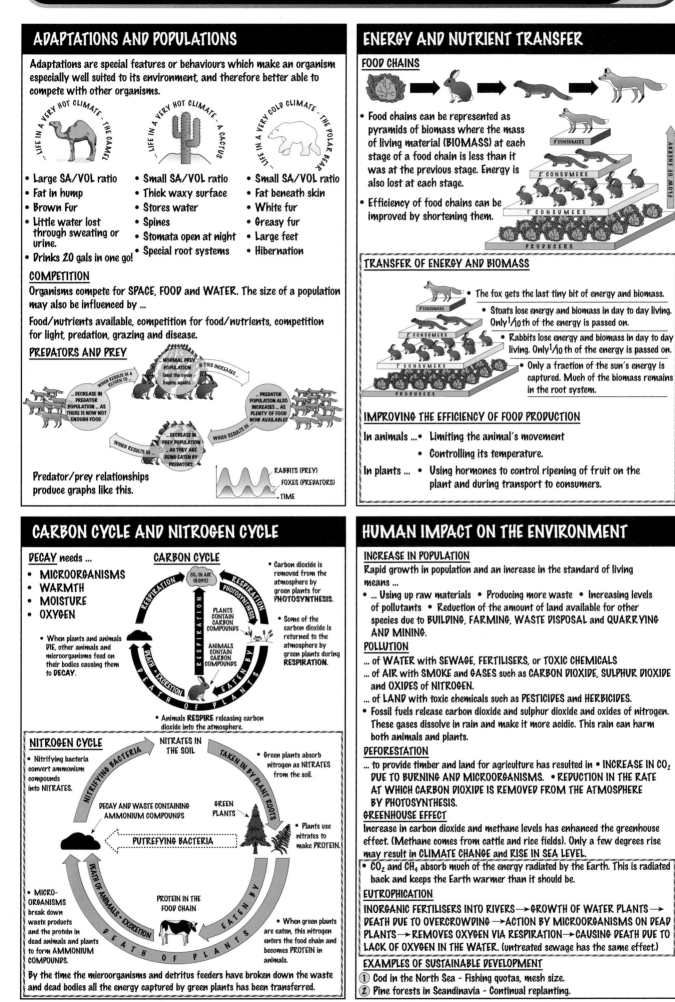

Predator/prey relationships produce graphs like this.

RABBITS (PREY)
FOXES (PREDATORS)
TIME

ENERGY AND NUTRIENT TRANSFER

FOOD CHAINS

- Food chains can be represented as pyramids of biomass where the mass of living material (BIOMASS) at each stage of a food chain is less than it was at the previous stage. Energy is also lost at each stage.
- Efficiency of food chains can be improved by shortening them.

3° CONSUMERS
2° CONSUMERS
1° CONSUMERS
PRODUCERS
FLOW OF ENERGY

TRANSFER OF ENERGY AND BIOMASS

- The fox gets the last tiny bit of energy and biomass.
- Stoats lose energy and biomass in day to day living. Only $1/10$ th of the energy is passed on.
- Rabbits lose energy and biomass in day to day living. Only $1/10$ th of the energy is passed on.
- Only a fraction of the sun's energy is captured. Much of the biomass remains in the root system.

IMPROVING THE EFFICIENCY OF FOOD PRODUCTION

In animals ...
- Limiting the animal's movement
- Controlling its temperature.

In plants ...
- Using hormones to control ripening of fruit on the plant and during transport to consumers.

CARBON CYCLE AND NITROGEN CYCLE

DECAY needs ...
- MICROORGANISMS
- WARMTH
- MOISTURE
- OXYGEN

CARBON CYCLE

CO_2 IN AIR (0.03%)

RESPIRATION
PHOTOSYNTHESIS
RESPIRATION
PLANTS CONTAIN CARBON COMPOUNDS
ANIMALS CONTAIN CARBON COMPOUNDS
DEATH + EXCRETION
DEATH OF PLANTS
EATEN BY PLANTS

- When plants and animals DIE, other animals and microorganisms feed on their bodies causing them to DECAY.

- Carbon dioxide is removed from the atmosphere by green plants for PHOTOSYNTHESIS.
- Some of the carbon dioxide is returned to the atmosphere by green plants during RESPIRATION.
- Animals RESPIRE releasing carbon dioxide into the atmosphere.

NITROGEN CYCLE

NITRATES IN THE SOIL
NITRIFYING BACTERIA
TAKEN IN BY PLANT ROOTS
GREEN PLANTS
DECAY AND WASTE CONTAINING AMMONIUM COMPOUNDS
PUTREFYING BACTERIA
PROTEIN IN THE FOOD CHAIN
DEATH OF ANIMALS + EXCRETION
DEATH OF PLANTS
EATEN BY

- Nitrifying bacteria convert ammonium compounds into NITRATES.
- Green plants absorb nitrogen as NITRATES from the soil.
- Plants use nitrates to make PROTEIN.
- MICRO-ORGANISMS break down waste products and the protein in dead animals and plants to form AMMONIUM COMPOUNDS.
- When green plants are eaten, this nitrogen enters the food chain and becomes PROTEIN in animals.

By the time the microorganisms and detritus feeders have broken down the waste and dead bodies all the energy captured by green plants has been transferred.

HUMAN IMPACT ON THE ENVIRONMENT

INCREASE IN POPULATION

Rapid growth in population and an increase in the standard of living means ...
- ... Using up raw materials • Producing more waste • Increasing levels of pollutants • Reduction of the amount of land available for other species due to BUILDING, FARMING, WASTE DISPOSAL and QUARRYING AND MINING.

POLLUTION

... of WATER with SEWAGE, FERTILISERS, or TOXIC CHEMICALS
... of AIR with SMOKE and GASES such as CARBON DIOXIDE, SULPHUR DIOXIDE and OXIDES OF NITROGEN
... of LAND with toxic chemicals such as PESTICIDES and HERBICIDES.
- Fossil fuels release carbon dioxide and sulphur dioxide and oxides of nitrogen. These gases dissolve in rain and make it more acidic. This rain can harm both animals and plants.

DEFORESTATION

... to provide timber and land for agriculture has resulted in • INCREASE IN CO_2 DUE TO BURNING AND MICROORGANISMS. • REDUCTION IN THE RATE AT WHICH CARBON DIOXIDE IS REMOVED FROM THE ATMOSPHERE BY PHOTOSYNTHESIS.

GREENHOUSE EFFECT

Increase in carbon dioxide and methane levels has enhanced the greenhouse effect. (Methane comes from cattle and rice fields). Only a few degrees rise may result in CLIMATE CHANGE and RISE IN SEA LEVEL.
- CO_2 and CH_4 absorb much of the energy radiated by the Earth. This is radiated back and keeps the Earth warmer than it should be.

EUTROPHICATION

INORGANIC FERTILISERS INTO RIVERS→GROWTH OF WATER PLANTS → DEATH DUE TO OVERCROWDING →ACTION BY MICROORGANISMS ON DEAD PLANTS →REMOVES OXYGEN VIA RESPIRATION→CAUSING DEATH DUE TO LACK OF OXYGEN IN THE WATER. (untreated sewage has the same effect.)

EXAMPLES OF SUSTAINABLE DEVELOPMENT

① Cod in the North Sea - Fishing quotas, mesh size.
② Pine forests in Scandinavia - Continual replanting.

SUMMARY QUESTIONS

1. a) Describe four organisms and how they are adapted to their environment.
    b) For one of your chosen organisms suggest the factors for which it may be competing in its habitat.

2. a) Name three factors that both animals and plants compete with each other for.
    b) What is a population?
    c) Name one factor that affects both the animal and plant population.
    d) Name one factor that affects the animal population but not the plant population.
    e) Name one factor that affects the plant population but not the animal population.

3. a) What are predators?
    b) What are prey?
    c) Describe the predator/prey cycle of lynx and hares.

4. The diagram below shows a simple food chain.

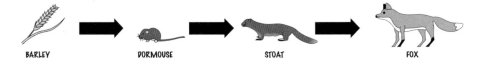

BARLEY   DORMOUSE   STOAT   FOX

    a) Which of the above is the producer?
    b) Where does the producer get its energy from?
    c) What is a pyramid of biomass?
    d) Apart from biomass, what else is lost at each stage of a food chain?

5. a) What happens to the amount of available energy and the amount of available biomass as you move up the food chain?
    b) Why does this happen?
    c) How can this knowledge be used to improve the efficiency of food production in animals?
    d) What can be done to improve the efficiency of food production in plants?

6. The diagram opposite shows the carbon cycle.
    a) Use the words RESPIRATION, PHOTOSYNTHESIS, EATEN BY, DEATH OF ANIMALS AND EXCRETION and DEATH OF PLANTS to label the processes A to G on the diagram opposite.
    b) What part do the following play in the cycle:
       i) Photosynthesis
       ii) Respiration
       iii) Transfer of carbon

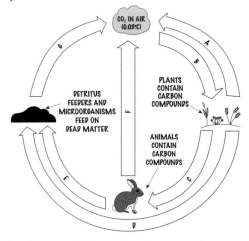

7. a) Microorganisms are a very important part of the Carbon Cycle. In what conditions do microorganisms work best?
    b) Think of a practical way to slow down the action of microorganisms.
    c) Give two important uses of microorganisms by humans.

8. a) Use the words TAKEN IN BY PLANT ROOTS, NITRIFYING BACTERIA, DEATH OF ANIMALS AND EXCRETION, DEATH OF PLANTS, EATEN BY, to label the processes A-E on the diagram opposite.
   b) How do animals get protein?
   c) If a special vaccine was discovered which could kill off ALL the microorganisms on the planet instantly what would be the effect of using this vaccine on the Nitrogen Cycle?

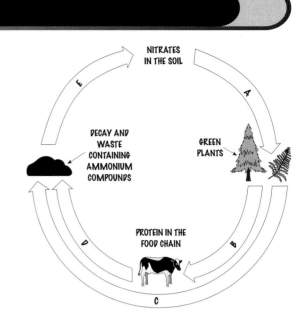

9. a) How has the land which was once occupied by a variety of animals and plants been reduced in quantity due to human activity?
   b) In what ways have human activities polluted ...
      i) water ii) air iii) land
   c) What are the consequences if waste is not properly handled and stored?
   d) When waste gases are released into the atmosphere they can cause acid rain. Name three sources of these gases.
   e) How is acid rain damaging to the environment?

10. a) In which two ways has deforestation increased the level of carbon dioxide in the atmosphere?
    b) What is the 'Greenhouse Effect'?
    c) What is it caused by?
    d) Deforestation is partly responsible for the Greenhouse Effect. Name four other contributory factors.
    e) What could the Greenhouse Effect eventually cause?

11. a) Describe the process of eutrophication, and explain how it can be avoided.
    b) What part do microorganisms play in the process of eutrophication?

12. a) In the mid-1970's stocks of cod in the North Sea were dwindling. What measures have been taken to ensure that stocks are replenished?
    b) Pine forests in Scandinavia have also reduced in number. What measures have been taken to ensure that stocks of pine forests do not dwindle any further?

13. a) Why is the Red Kite an endangered bird?
    b) What can be done to protect endangered species?

Lonsdale SRG SCIENCE REVISION GUIDES

THE COMPLETE KEY STAGE 3 PACKAGE ...

... 3 Course books

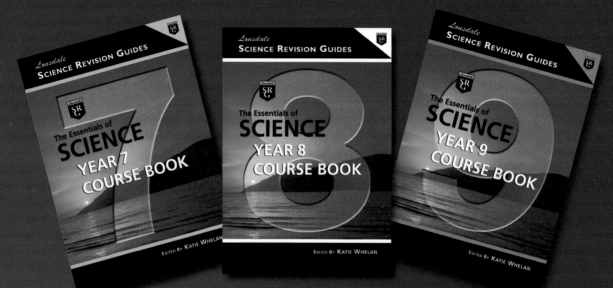

... matched perfectly to the QCA exemplar scheme of work for Key Stage 3.
All the content ... lots of exercises ... and an investigation for each unit.
These course books provide an inspection-proof scheme of work
for over-worked Science Departments.
Also there are 300 pages of differentiated internet support!

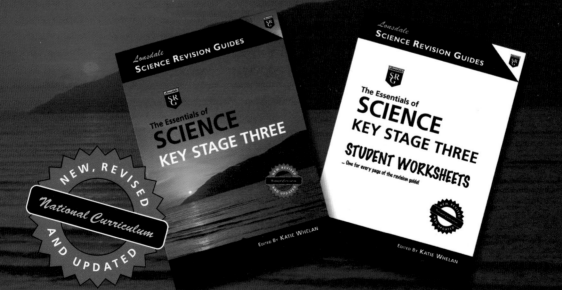

Plus ... the world famous **Revision Guide** and **Student Worksheets**.
These pull together all the information pupils need from years 7, 8 and 9 for
their Key Stage 3 National Curriculum Tests. They are completely revised and
updated for the new National Curriculum and contain everything the pupil
needs to revise ... and nothing more.